The
QUANTOCKS

J R Hulbert
2013

Other books written, co-written or edited by the same author include:

Locational Analysis in Human Geography (1965)
Frontiers in Geographical Teaching (1965)
Models in Geography (1967)
Network Analysis in Geography (1969)
Regional Forecasting (1971)
Geography: A Modern Synthesis (1972)
Elements of Spatial Structure (1975)
Locational Models (1977)
Locational Methods (1977)
Spatial Diffusion (1981)
Dictionary of Human Geography (1981)
Spread of Measles in Fiji and the Pacific (1985)
Spatial Aspects of Influenza Epidemics (1986)
Atlas of Disease Distributions (1988)
The Geographer's Art (1990)
Historical Geography of a Major Human Virus Disease (1993)
Deciphering Global Epidemics (1998)
Swedish Research in Human Geography (1999)
Island Epidemics (2000)
The Geographical Structure of Epidemics (2000)
Geography: A Global Synthesis (2001)
World Atlas of Epidemic Diseases (2004)
Infectious Diseases: A Geographical Analysis (2009)

Peter Haggett

The
QUANTOCKS

Biography of an English Region

Photographs by Jackie Haggett

THE POINT WALTER PRESS

Detail from a carved bench-end in a Quantock parish church (Holy Ghost, Crowcombe) *c.*1534 (see Plate 1). The symbol was suggested by a lino-cut of the carving by John F. Lawrence made four centuries later and reproduced in Berta Lawrence *Quantock Country* (1952).

First published in 2012 by
Peter Haggett at The Point Walter Press.

For copies of the book contact:
www.the-quantocks.com
pointwalterpress@gmail.com
or write to the author at 5 Tun Bridge Close,
Chew Magna, Somerset, BS40 8SU.

ISBN 978-0-9573352-0-2

Designed by Charlie Webster at Production Line, Minster Lovell
Photoset in Bembo

Printed by Berforts Information Press, Eynsham, Oxford

CONTENTS

For Brenda
with love from us both

Preface

A REMEMBERED EARTH

Once in a life a man ought to concentrate his mind upon the remembered
earth. He ought to give himself up to a particular landscape of his experience,
to look at it from as many angles as he can, to wonder about it, to dwell
upon it. He ought to imagine he touches it with his hands at every season
... to recollect all the colours of the dawn and dusk.
N. Scott Momaday *The Way to Rainy Mountain* (1969)[1]

My remembered earth is the Quantocks. I must have first seen the hills over the
side of a high pram in 1933 well before my conscious recollections began. But
in childhood and schooldays their presence was a constant theme. My home, like
almost all the Haggett forebears I can trace, lay at the northern end of the
Polden Hills in central Somerset. From the low rise of Gaunts Hill – itself a low
'island' rising from the Somerset Levels – there, across the great meander sweeps
of the River Parrett, lay a wilder landscape which beckoned and demanded to
be explored. For most seasons of the year the sun set behind the range of the
Quantock Hills and from my attic bedroom I could see their undulating dark
blue profile like the flat of a stage set marking my western horizon. Time spent
in that western hill country was one of the joys of my schooldays: walking,
cycling, fossil-hunting, dam building, and camping (permits from the Forestry
Commission and the Fairfield Estate office were readily given). This pleasure
even extended into my university years at Cambridge. A foxed copy of a second-
year dissertation is a reminder that, after pouring over old maps in the Somerset
County Archives (then held in the old Taunton Shire Hall), I wrote my required
10,000 words on historical changes in the use of land in the Quantock
parishes.[2]

That summer of 1952 was to be critical in the genesis of this little book
written sixty summers later. In my first year at Cambridge, I had just completed
my Qualifying exams and had – by some unlikely alchemy – done well enough
to be awarded a five guineas book prize by my college. Two volumes had to be

chosen and submitted for cover stamping with the college crest, in my case the barbed wheel of St Catharine of Alexandria. The choice was easy. Berta Lawrence, novelist, essayist, poet and wife of my old history master, had just published that Spring her *Quantock Country*, an enchanting evocation of an area I loved. And then the year before, a new edition of H. C. Darby's classic *An Historical Geography of England before A.D. 1800* had been published but whose price meant it lay beyond my means.[3] But with riches to spend, both volumes could just be afforded and I rushed to Heffers Bookshop in Petty Cury to secure them and bring them back in triumph to St Catharine's to have the crest stamped and 'bene merente. Sanctae Catharinae alumno' plates added. Six decades later, this book is a long overdue tribute to both authors.

After graduation, my trade as a professional geographer took me away from Somerset: first to University College London (where Darby was my Head of Department), then back to Cambridge as a college don, then to the chair at Bristol which served as my university base over the next forty years. These three places were to be base camps which allowed me to teach in a score of overseas universities from Berkeley in California, through Brunei in Borneo, to Canberra in Australia and to research in field areas from Brazil via the sub-Arctic to the Pacific islands.

But the seeds Berta Lawrence (and her husband, Jack, who taught me history) had sown remained in my mind. Many summer holidays walking the Quantock ridges and combes followed and, like Virginia Woolf,[4] our honeymoon was spent at Holford and in due course our four children had to endure my enthusiasm for dam-building on Quantock streams. Now my last 'academic' research volume completed, my last committee chaired, my last research report filed, I've had time to return to the Quantocks and to write the little book that has lain at the back of my mind for so long. Its title retains elements of both the books that inspired it. For it is a period by period account, a historical geography in Darby's sense, of the changing geography of a small *pays* (a distinct region) set within the broader structure of the county within which I was born, bred, and schooled and where I have lived for much of my eight decades.

I'm not a historian, as Jack Lawrence would confirm, still less a prehistorian and so its presumptuous to try and span so many centuries (even millennia) in the Quantock story. So I've had to rely heavily – as do others writing about Somerset – on the writings of a small group of distinguished historians and archaeologists who have revolutionized our understanding of the county over the last several decades. They include Mick Aston, Robin Bush, Robert Dunning, Leslie Grinsell, Tom Mayberry, Heather Riley, and Mary Siraut. To those should be added the natural historians, Ernest Neal and Philip Radford, who have thrown fresh light on Quantock wildlife. Without their work this small book simply could not have been attempted. And then there are those archivists and librarians going back to I. P. Collis (who introduced me as a student to Somerset tithe maps in the Shire Hall archives) and David Bromwich and members of his staff at the Somerset Library Taunton who devilled out sources. I hope they will not find too many errors in my amateur interpretations.

Those who care for the Quantock's great country houses have been uniformly helpful. I'm grateful to Lady Gass for welcoming me to the family house at Fairfield and to the late Michael Stancomb, Sir Walter and Lady Luttrell and Katherine Wyndham for showing me Barford Park, The Court House, and Orchard Wyndham. I'm also hugely indebted to those who have been kind enough to read portions of the text, spot errors and suggest improvements: John Allen, Peter Braine, Lady Gass, Iain Porter, Hugh Prudden, David and Sheila Rabson, Ian Simmons and Ivor and Pam Slocombe have all gone beyond the call of friendship to do this. Any book which attempts to cover 400 million years in 200 pages is bound to include many errors of fact and interpretation: those that remain are mine alone. My old Oxford editor, John Davey, encouraged me to publish the work and secured Charlie Webster of Production Line who has put so much thought into making the finished book so attractive. Formal permissions for reproduction rights are listed elsewhere but I must especially thank Jean Rees's daughter for agreeing to the use of 'Barford Park' on the cover of this book and to Chris Lawrence for permission to use material from his mother's *Quantock Country*.

My greatest debt is to my daughter, Jack. She has spent hours, days and weeks in the Quantocks with her cameras waiting for the right light and getting into corners that the years had now put beyond my easy reach. Her photographic record (only a fragment of the thousands of images are reproduced here) will outlast her father's words and I'm more grateful to her than I can say. I know that she in turn wishes to thank Sarah McAuslan-Crine, then head of nursing at the Intensive Care Unit at the Bristol Royal Infirmary, for granting a year's career break to study photography in 2008. At Filton College, tutors Nick Bright, Karen Brett, Steve Ellaway, John Stubbs and Martin Puddy provided invaluable help; Karen was also kind enough to comment since on the Quantock work. Finally, she owes a special debt to Jai Logan Gallen who helped so patiently with file organization, new photo-computer programmes, and website development.

We are both grateful to those at Beach Cottage, Blackmore Farm, Combe House, Curry Pool Mill, Fulford Grange, Gurney Manor Mill, Manor Farm, Parsonage Farm, Quantock House, Wick House and Windser Farm plus the youth hostel at Pardlestone, Kilve (now sadly closed). All have provided shelter and warm Quantock hospitality, some over many stays.

Finally, my family both here and in Australia have tolerated my passion for all things 'Quantockian' over many years: indeed my youngest son met his bride-to-be at Great Wood Camp. All of them will be relieved to learn the book is now finished and that my excuses for postponing many garden and household tasks are now exhausted. As for Brenda, my debt is unpayable: after enduring my writing a score of books over the fifty-six years of our married life together, there are simply no words left. This last volume is dedicated to her with love, admiration and gratitude – from the both of us.

PETER HAGGETT
Chew Magna, Somerset.
Lady Day 2012.

ACKNOWLEDGEMENTS

The author wishes to thank the following who have kindly given permission to reproduce or redraw copyright graphic material:

Mrs Jenny Sharman for permission to use Jean Rees's painting of 'Barford Park' on the cover of this volume and in Fig. 1.11; Sedgemoor District Council for Figs. 1.2, 7.13, and 8.6; Charles Scribner for Fig. 1.4; National Portrait Gallery for Fig. 1.4; Bristol Evening Post for Fig. 1.10; The Tate Gallery, London, for Fig. 1.11 and Fig. 6.7; Victoria County History of Somerset for Figs. 1.16, 4.12, and 5.5; British Geological Survey (License IPR/148–63CV (All rights reserved) for Figs. 2.1. 2.2, and 2.3; John Wiley & Sons and the *Geographical Journal*, for Fig. 2.5; Prof. Penning-Rowsell for Fig. 2.6; Mike Jones for Fig. 2.10; Hugh Prudden for Fig. 2.11; Hazel Riley and English Heritage for Figs. 3.3, 3.4 and 4.4; Museum of Somerset and Somerset Museums Service for Fig. 3.6; Cambridge University Press for Fig. 4.3; Somerset Archaeological Society for Fig. 4.10; *The Builder* archives for Fig. 4.14; Lady Gass for Fig. 5.3; Hestercombe Gardens Trust for Figs. 5.8 and 7.1; University of Manchester, Whitworth Gallery, for Fig. 5.8; Peter Barnfield and the West Somerset Railway (WSR) for Fig. 7.15; Electricité de France (EDF) for Fig. 7.9.

He is also grateful to those who have given permission for short passages to be quoted from published works: University of New Mexico Press for Thomas Momaday's *The Way to Rainy Mountain* (Preface); John Murray for Freya Stark's *Traveller's Prelude* (Chap. 1); Chris Lawrence for quotations from Berta Lawrence *Quantock Country* (Chap. 1) and the poem 'Exit from Cleeve' (Chap. 4); Robert Hale for Vincent Waite's *Portrait of the Quantocks* (Chap. 2); the Halsgrove Group (Somerset Books) for quotations from Tom Mayberry and Hilary Binding's *Somerset; The Millenium Book* and (Chaps. 4, 5 and 7); The Dovecote Press for the Nunzio Notaro quotation (Chap.7).

Attempts have been made by the author to trace and to contact all copyright holders for material used in the book but -- with the passage of time -- some leads have gone cold and a few sources have defeated him. There are also cases where letters have been sent but no response obtained. He apologizes for any permissions inadvertently missed and would be grateful if these could be brought to his attention to allow corrections to be made in any future printings.

One

Prelude: A QUANTOCK TAPESTRY

If we could make contours in our hearts – as we do in maps – to see their loves, we should learn what strange unexpected regions attain the greatest depths. Often we might discover that a place rather than a person holds the secret.

Freya Stark, *Traveller's Prelude* (1950)[1]

This book is a biography, not of a person but of a place – a region, or what the French would call a *pays* (an area of country in which life and land are intrinsically linked). Like all biographies it tries to find and portray the distinctive character of the subject, to show what gives it a special flavour. Also, like all biographies, it tells a story with a procession over time conventionally arranged from early years to later. But here the parallel ends. For rather than the three-score-years-and-ten of a human life, the life of a region reaches back far more deeply in the past, even to the geological roots of the physical landscape itself. Even when the human actors come onto this environmental stage, the origins date back over 10,000 years and the story is told not of a single life but of the choreography of intertwining life-paths over generation after generation. It is this bundle of lives, a few known but most unknown, which have shaped and reshaped the landscape we see today.

The land whose story I've chosen to tell we call by its simplest regional name, the 'Quantocks': a name which encompasses both the Quantock Hills themselves and the wider skirt of lowland that abuts them. Other writers have termed this wider range of territory the 'land of Quantock', 'Quantock country' or even – in a Wagnerian moment – the 'Quantock oberland'.[2] As Fig. 1.1 shows, it lies in the western part of the county of Somersetshire in the southwest of England. As shown on this map it covers 140 square miles, an area around one half the size of Exmoor National Park or a third of Dartmoor.

Like Caesar's Gaul in my Latin lessons, the Quantocks can be divided into three parts. At its core lies a range of hills, the Quantock Hills that run for about

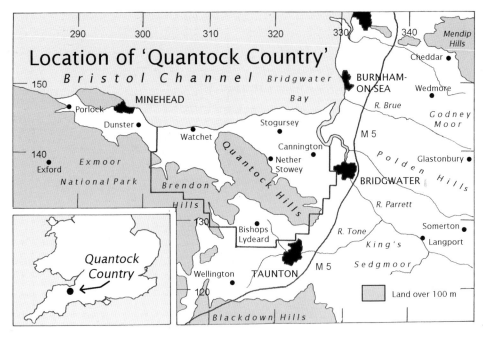

Fig.1.1 Map of Quantock country in its regional setting. The three main bordering towns (Bridgwater, Minehead and Taunton) are shown together with major transport and elevation features. The heavy line encloses the geographical area treated in this book. (Inset) Quantock country in relation to the rest of southern Britain.

twelve miles from the coast of the Bristol Channel at Quantoxhead south and east towards the Vale of Taunton Deane. The hills in their northern sections are rather narrow with steep flanks on the western side and deeply dissected valleys (locally called 'combes') on the eastern side. They reach their highest point at Wills Neck at 1,260 feet. In the southern third of their range, the hills fan out from two to five miles in width with lower heights and softer profiles.

To the east of the Quantock Hills, the land slopes away northwards towards the Bristol Channel and eastwards towards the River Parrett. If forms a piedmont area of rolling country below 300 feet with the occasional distinctive hill such as Cannington Park. The land is mostly in agricultural use with a scatter of small woodlots. Settlements form a line along the break of slope with the hill country but then a more random pattern with Stogursey, Nether Stowey and Cannington as the three leading settlements.

On the western side of the hill ridge the land is slightly higher and more rugged than the eastern piedmont. The most distinctive feature is the corridor, the Crowcombe corridor, which runs from the Vale of Taunton Deane northwards towards the coast at Blue Anchor and Watchet. This rises locally to rounded knolls and ridges over 500 feet. Further west the land rises up towards Exmoor to form the Brendon Hills. Although the prevailing land use here is agricultural, the proportion of woodland is higher occupying steep valleyside slopes and areas of poor soils. As in the east, there is a line of villages along the break of slope with the hill ridge and then a more random scatter of villages and hamlets across the rest of the area. The coastal port of Watchet with its inland twin of Williton in the north and Bishops Lydeard in the south are the two largest settlements.

In this opening chapter we ask four questions. First, what are the threads which give colour and character to the Quantocks? Second, what does the name mean and when did it first occur? Third, what area does it cover? Fourth, how is the book organized?

SEVEN STRANDS IN THE TAPESTRY

Knowing that I'm writing a book about this tiny geographical area ('you could lose it within Boston') an American colleague asks 'Why put time aside to write about the Quantocks? You drive past them on the M5 in twenty minutes'. I have two stock answers: that my family roots run deep in this part of the world and that, to a geographer (my lifelong trade), any piece of country has a story to tell if you dig deeply enough. But neither reason convinces him so I begin to list why the Quantock region deserves a biography – and stop at seven. I find they range oddly from Quantock dragons (Plate 1), through a poetic partnership (Plate 5A) to nuclear power (Plate15A). Here they are: others might choose a different seven.

Strand one: a modest beauty

The first reason for writing about the Quantocks is the intrinsic beauty of the landscape. Its hills and valleys crop up in every subsequent chapter so I suggest here that turning the pages of the colour photos in Plates 2, 3 and 4 will serve better than my words. Fig. 1.2 summarizes some of its essential landscape elements.[3] These are the reasons why it was England's first area to be formally designated as an Area of Outstanding Natural Beauty (AONB) in 1956, later to be joined by the Cotswolds, the Weald of Kent, the Lincolnshire Wolds. Unlike national parks, AONBs do not have their own planning authorities but are administered by the local authorities within which they lie, in our case the Somerset County Council. Over thirty were created in England in the next half-century, the most recent being the Tamar Valley in 1994.

But if the Quantock Hills had 'outstanding beauty' why were they not made part of Exmoor National Park created under the same legislation (the National Parks and Access to the Countryside Act, 1949) only two years earlier? The answer is twofold. First, they very nearly were. Serious consideration was given to drawing in the Quantocks Hills within national park boundaries. Inclusion

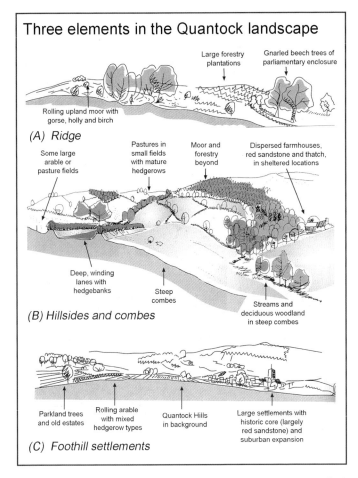

Three elements in the Quantock landscape

Large forestry plantations

Gnarled beech trees of parliamentary enclosure

Rolling upland moor with gorse, holly and birch

(A) Ridge

Pastures in small fields with mature hedgerows

Moor and forestry beyond

Dispersed farmhouses, red sandstone and thatch, in sheltered locations

Some large arable or pasture fields

Deep, winding lanes with hedgebanks

Steep combes

Streams and deciduous woodland in steep combes

(B) Hillsides and combes

Parkland trees and old estates

Rolling arable with mixed hedgerow types

Quantock Hills in background

Large settlements with historic core (largely red sandstone) and suburban expansion

(C) Foothill settlements

Fig. 1.2 Three elements in the Quantock landscape. A Quantock ridge. B Hillsides and combes. C Foothill settlements. Source: Sedgemoor District Council, 2003 (note 3), 98, 114, 119.

foundered not on the quality of its hill landscape for, as we see in Chapter 2, this formed a natural eastwards extension of the Exmoor landscape developed on the same Devonian rocks. The problem was that they could only be included as an outlier for the lowland corridor that separated it from the Brendons and the main Exmoor massif did not fit the National Park criteria. Today the easternmost edge of Exmoor's park boundary stops less than three miles short of the main Quantock ridge.[4]

A second reason is more subtle. As Berta Lawrence puts it: 'Quantock country will not appeal to those who admire only the magnificent and grandiose'. She sees its qualities as modest and understated, dependant on the changes wrought by the cycle of the seasons:

Its beauty is simple and unsophisticated, the motif of its pattern constantly repeated... red earth and green grass, apple orchards and stockyards, farm and round-pillared byre, roofs of thatch and russet tiles, brown barn and cider-house, colour-washed cottage and rose-red church, red herds and white flocks, deep red lanes, tilted red banks, and running streams, combe and wood and heathery moorland, That is all.[5]

An earlier Quantock writer, W. L. Nichols, described it a 'cheerful' landscape and contrasts it with the serious mien of highland mountains or Scottish glens (which he considered overrated). Fig. 1.3 gives an example from the upland ridge near Holford. Maxwell Fraser follows a similar theme, describing the Quantocks as an area of 'rich contentment' where 'an air of happy serenity' penetrates to every village with life flowing on quietly and unpretentiously.[6] It is typical in such writing that there is a counterpoint between the physical and human landscapes, both the hills and the settlements that surround them seem to be drawn in the same restrained and delicate colours.

Fig. 1.3 Example of the 'Quantock ridge' landscape: type 'A' in Fig. 1.2. Dowsborough (also called Danesborough) looking south from Hare Knap with a cairn, possibly of Bronze Age origin, in the foreground.

Strand two: an 'annus mirabilis'

It was in this gentle landscape that a poetic explosion rocked the literary world at the end of the eighteenth century (Fig. 1.4). As recalled in *The Prelude*:

> Upon smooth Quantocks airy ridge we roved
> Unchecked, or loitered mid their sylvan combs,
> Thou in bewitching words, with happy art,
> Did'st chaunt the vision of that Antient man,
> The bright-eyed Mariner, and rueful woes
> Didst utter of the Lady Christabel.[7]

The words are by William Wordsworth, the 'thou' in the verse refers to Samuel Taylor Coleridge, and the poems are the 'Rhyme of the Ancient

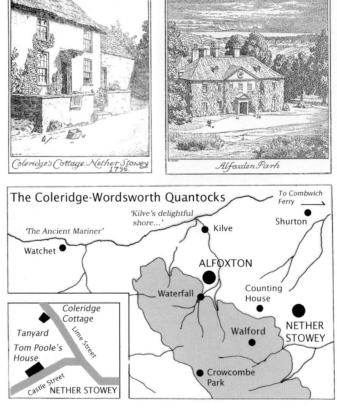

Fig. 1.4 *The Coleridge-Wordsworth Quantocks. Coleridge's cottage at Nether Stowey* (above left). *Alfoxton* (above right), *rented by the Wordsworths from the St Aubyn family (see also Plate 5A). Map showing main locations associated with the Coleridge-Wordsworth friendship in the years 1797-8 (below), with inset map showing Coleridge's cottage and Tom Poole's tanyard in Nether Stowey. Source: Prints by A.H.New, in Knight, 1914 (note 8).*

Mariner' and 'Christabel'. The results of these musings on Quantock walks by Coleridge and Wordsworth was to lead to the publication of *Lyrical Ballads* (1798), a volume which is a milestone in English poetry.

The story of that partnership has been told and retold and if overseas visitors have ever heard about the Quantocks then it is likely to be due to two men and one year: Coleridge, Wordsworth, and the *annus mirabilis* of 1797-98.[8] Samuel Taylor Coleridge (1772-1834) was an English poet, son of the vicar of Ottery St Mary in nearby Devon (Fig. 1.5).[9] After the statutory unhappy childhood he went up to Jesus College, Cambridge, to study for the church but interrupted this by enlisting in the Dragoons. The start of his romantic and revolutionary ideas probably date to 1794 when he met Robert Southey on a walking tour. Their revolutionary ideas of founding a communist society (a 'pantisocracy') in Pennsylvania predictably came to nothing and the following year he married Southey's friend, Sarah Fricker. In financial difficulties, he accepted a generous offer from Tom Poole of Nether Stowey to move to a cottage in Lime Street. The year was 1797, Sarah was pregnant, and Coleridge was just 25.

Later that same year Coleridge met with the poet William Wordsworth (1770-1850) and his sister Dorothy who were living in Dorset. Wordsworth was then 27 and his sister 28. Their momentous decision to also move to the Quantocks (to the vacant St Aubyn home at Alfoxton [Plate 5A] only three miles to the north) lead to a close friendship. 'We are three people but only one soul' as Wordsworth

Fig. 1.5 The poets Samuel Taylor Coleridge aged 24 (left) and William Wordsworth aged 28 (right). Both sketches are drawn in coloured chalks and pencil by Robert Hancock in 1796 and 1798 respectively, i.e. near the time of the annus mirabilis. A third figure, Dorothy Wordsworth, cannot be shown as no contemporary portrait of her from that period can be traced: a silhouette from Dove Cottage is later. Source: © National Portrait Gallery, London. See note 9.

put it. It also sparked a period of intensive discussion and rethinking which saw the prevailing neo-classicism rejected in favour of the 'Romantic' style. When *Lyrical Ballads* was published the next year by Joseph Cottle at Bristol, it represented a Quantock-based manifesto which opened with Coleridge's 'Ancient Mariner' and closed with Wordsworth's 'Tintern Abbey'.

The small cottage at Nether Stowey was the unlikely crucible of verse which continues to hold a place in every current English anthology as Coleridge's greatest. Not only the major marine narrative of the 'Ancient Mariner' but poignant reflections on loneliness in 'This lime tree bower my prison', 'Fears in solitude', 'The nightingale', and the magical wanderings to the mysterious Xanadu in 'Kubla Khan'. How far laudanum and how far the Quantock landscape powered his imagination will remain a source of debate amongst scholars and critics. Certainly what survives of Dorothy Wordsworth's diary for the year (the original has been lost) suggests that their walks together 'on Quantock's ridge' or 'by Kilve's delightful shore' played its part. The significance of the partnership was augmented by the large circle of mainly young friends who came to visit them there: poet Robert Southey, essayist Charles Lamb, publisher Joseph Cottle, scientist Humphrey Davey.

Dorothy began her now famous journal 'to give William pleasure' and entries for the period from January 20th to March 22nd survive with, in addition, nineteen letters (seven by William, the rest by Dorothy) from the Alfoxton year. They include William's reactions to the Quantock spring, in a letter written to his Bristol publisher, Joseph Cottle (12th April 1798): 'Within four days the season has advanced with greater rapidity than I ever remember, and the country becomes almost every hour more lovely'. Dorothy's lamented to Mrs Rawson in a letter dated 13th June 1798 about having to leave 'that dear and beautiful place'.[10]

But within a year it was over. The Wordsworth's strange behaviour and nightly wanderings lead to them being suspected as French spies and Alfoxton's aristocratic and patriotic owner refused to extend the lease for a further year. The Wordsworths moved on to Germany to study Schiller's works and by 1800 Coleridge (increasingly at odds with Sarah) had settled at Keswick in the Lake District. A new phase of work in a new location was beginning for both poets. Today the house at Alfoxton is in private hands but the small Coleridge cottage at Nether Stowey can be visited and the National Trust is steadily improving the range of exhibition materials on display there.

Strand three: the lore of the land

Long before the 'annus mirabilis' tales of a different sort were circulating in the Quantocks. The area is one of the richest in England in terms of legend and folklore (see Fig. 1.6). Like the accumulation of lichens on an old tree or of many species in an old hedgerow, a richness of legend speaks of antiquity and of

Fig. 1.6   Pagan fertility symbols in the Quantocks were interlinked with Christian buildings. 'Green man' carving on a sixteenth-century benchend in Crowcombe church (left). A female fertility figure (called a 'Sheila-na-gig') (right) carved in stone embedded in the south wall of parish church of St Martin of Tours at Fiddington.

long human occupation of a landscape. As my Icelandic friends argue, the deeper the accumulation of tales and fables, the older and longer-settled the region of that island. Judged by this metric, the Quantocks stand out as a very old part of the English countryside and as such has proved a honeypot for legend collectors such as Ruth Tongue in her *Somerset Folklore* and Berta Lawrence in her *Somerset Legends*.[11] A few samples to give a flavour of this tradition.

The 'Great Road' across the northern hills from Staple via Longstone Hill down to Holford is a legend-rich path (Fig. 1.7). Although curtly dismissed by serious scholars, the various legends which surround the supposed journey of Joseph of Arimithea (a tin merchant from the Holy Land) to Glastonbury persist. Tongue in her notes on 'Oral traditions, Crowcombe and Holford, 1901' records a version which relates to the Quantocks:

> Our Lord as a boy came voyaging with a sailor uncle to Britain. Their trading ship put in at Watchet and from there he walked across the Quantocks to Bridgwater where He boarded a punt and crossed the lakes and marshes to the foot of Mendip, ending his journey high up at Priddy.[12]

She also relates how even in the last century the 'Great Road' across the northern Quantocks continued to be referred to as 'Our Lord's Path' by a very old Holford resident. Needless to say, versions of essentially the same legend exist in fifteen other places, mostly in Cornwall (e.g. St Just in Roseland).

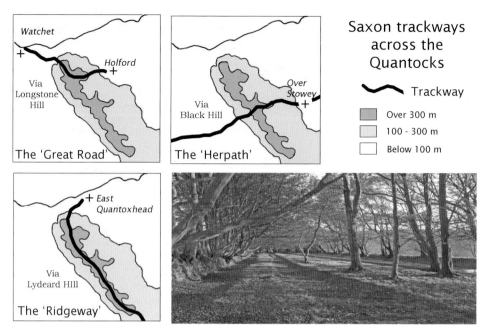

Fig. 1.7 Trackways across the Quantock Hills were certainly in place by Saxon times and may have been of far greater antiquity. Approximate routes are shown. Photo (lower right) *shows a section of the ridgeway near Crowcombe Gate.*

Shervage Wood, a mile to the south of the village of Holford and dissected today by the A39 trunk road, is now owned by the National Trust. According to local tradition this wood was once home to a long, wingless dragon (see the benchend in Plate 1). It was of a type known as a 'worm' and so fierce that the local woodcutter dared not go there to cut wood. But desperately needing money, he eventually took the risk. All went well in the morning, so at noon he took his first rest on a log among the bracken. But the log shook under him. In desperation the woodcutter leapt to his feet: 'So thee do movey, do 'ee! Take that then!' and sank his axe into it.

Some versions of the legend say the dragon died, others that it was cut into two halves one of which wriggled off to Kingston St Mary (at the southern end of the hills) where it re-appeared to give a separate dragon legend there. In the Kingston form it was killed by rolling a boulder down Buncombe combe which stuck in the beast's gullet, dousing the fire and killing the dragon. The Shervage dragon at Crowcombe church is complemented by a carving on the corner of Bishops Lydeard church tower (a parish adjoining Kingston) which probably records the boulder legend.

While most Quantock traditions date back to early in the medieval period, others are sixteenth-century in origin.[13] Two concern some of the region's oldest land-owning families in the region, the Sydenhams and the Wyndhams.

One of the strangest Quantock stories concerns Combe Sydenham to the west of the region and the Elizabethan navigator and privateer, Sir Francis Drake (1540-1596). This was the family home of Drake's wife, Elizabeth Sydenham. She stayed there while Drake was away on one of his circumnavigating voyages which lasted so long that her father – assuming Drake was by now dead – persuaded her to accept a proposal from another suitor. As the wedding guests gathered in nearby Stogumber church, Drake (by some magic radar) learnt of his wife's plans and fired from the Pacific a ship's cannon in anger.

Some versions of the story say the ball rolled into the porch of Combe Sydenham Hall as the bride was leaving, for Stogumber church; others that it landed on the altar steps as the bride was coming up the aisle. At all events, the wedding was called off and Drake eventually returned. Until recently Sydenham Hall proudly displayed a large meteorite (now in the Museum of Somerset) and tales about the 'cannonball' claim include one that it will return to the Hall in times of national danger; perhaps a variant of the Drake's Drum legend from nearby Devon.

The Wyndham family have a long association with this area illustrated by the great Wyndham family chapel in the parish church of Watchet, St Decumans (see Fig. 5.4). C. H. Poole's early book on Somerset folklore retells the story from 1559 of a Florence Wyndham who fell into such a deep coma that it was assumed she was dead. Her coffin lay overnight in St Decuman's church prior to the funeral and interment in the family vault. An unscrupulous sexton tried to steal valuable rings from her fingers and tried a knife when he could not pull them off. The pain from the cut roused Florence from her coma so that she sat up, causing the terrified sexton to flee (and later throw himself over the cliffs at Watchet). Florence Wyndham lived for many years and gave birth to a son from whom the later line of distinguished Wyndhams are descended.

Such tales formed part of story-telling tradition that gave local colour to a region in a pre-literate and pre-TV age. In the Quantocks such stories abounded: grave robbers at Cannington, a white dove fluttering at a Williton window, Midsummer Eve wraiths at Crowcombe, the magical cider mug at Stogursey, bewitched toads of Broomfield, goblins at Ruborough Camp are all remembered. Under the historian's stern gaze other tales – that Jane Seymour, wife of Henry VIII, was born at West Bower manor (the home of the Seymours from 1489 until 1552) in Durleigh parish or that Halsway manor was Cardinal Beaufort's hunting lodge – have been disproved. I hope a modicum of Quantock legends will long survive unscathed to continue to add their colour to its landscape.

Strand four: Quantock parish churches

Quantock parish churches contain (despite the heavy restoration in the Victorian period, described in Chapter 6), so much of early interest that it's hard to know where to start. Their towers alone deserve a book. But I choose here just two features which give this area of Somerset a special flavour: carved bench-ends within the church and churchyard monuments and trees outside.

In church interiors, one takes today's orderly sets of pews for granted so it's hard to recall that fixed benches were uncommon until the late Medieval period. Highest ranking pews were built close to the pulpit and the altar, with many box pews constructed for and owned by leading families within the parish. A rich feature of the Quantock churches is the intricately-carved ends of such oak benches. Peter Poyntz Wright in his *Rural Benchends of Somerset* describes 220 surviving examples across the county and of these over a third relate to Quantock churches.[14] Fig. 1.8 maps the distribution of such churches with Bishops Lydeard leading the pack with fifteen examples and five other parish churches (Kingston St Mary in the south, Crowcombe and Monksilver in the west, East Quantoxhead in the north, and Spaxton and Stogursey in the east) with half or more that number. Subjects range from birds and animals to people, from abstract leaf patterns to religious symbols. All are worth visiting.

Most carvings appear to date from the mid sixteenth to the mid seventeenth centuries. For all the Somerset carvings, only two names of those who did the work are known and both are Quantock men. Simon Warman of Bicknoller left his signed name on a benchend in Broomfield church (see Fig.1.8). The distinctive edge mouldings that surround the name are found in many other bench ends in the southern Quantocks and Taunton Deane suggesting that he was a master carver whose work was in wide demand in the area. A second carver with the surname Glosse, is mentioned in the Stogursey church records in 1524 in relation to the purchase of imported oak boards from Wales and he may well have been responsible for the fine set of carvings which can be seen in that church. Their depiction of rural life in the Quantocks is shown at later points in this book (see Fig. 4.12, 5.11, 8.4).

Churchyards with their memorials and ancient trees are a second theme. There are few better ways of sensing the deep legacy of the lives that have shaped the Quantocks than wandering around their churchyards. Despite Victorian stuffiness, earlier memorials allow life to be seen as comic as well as tragic. One of my favorite churches is Bicknoller nestling on the western flank of the hills (Figure 1.9).[15] One memorial on the outside of the south porch laments the ever-changing times:

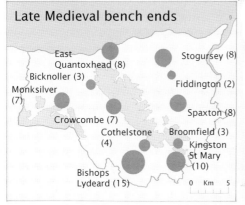

Fig.1.8 Medieval bench-ends are one of the glories of Quantock medieval parish churches. South aisle of Bishops Lydeard parish church (above). Simon Warman of Bicknoller (lower right) was one of the carvers who left his name on this pew end in Broomfield parish church. Numbers on the map refer to those listed in Wright, 1983 (note 14). Other examples are given in Plate 1 and Figs. 4.12, 5.11, 8.4 and 8.11.

> O, who would trust the world
>   or prize what's in it,
> That gives and takes
>   and chops and changes ev'ry minit.

Even the straight-laced Commonwealth period brought its touches of humour in the strained rhyming of the family epitaph for the parish minister Bartholomew Safford (1643, 1646-62):

> Here lie three Saffords out of view, Mabel, Mary, Bartholomew.
> Bartholomew Safford's flesh and bone, His wife, His sister and His son.
> Mabel became for worms a bait, December 9th in forty-eight.

Mary was fitted for the bier, On March 4th that same year.
Death on Bartholomew did fixe, On March the 2nd fifty-six.
Wife, Sister, Brother, Father dear, Christ's minister and parson here.'

In the churchyard lies George Jones, the village blacksmith, who died in 1808, and whose verse concludes wearily 'My nails are drove, my work is done'. I covet such an epitaph.

Yew trees (*Taxus baccata*) were traditionally planted in Quantock, as in most English churchyards, on the southern side of the church and rarely on the eastern side where they were thought to interfere with the departure of souls. A source of timber for medieval longbows but with berries deadly to grazing cattle, the churchyard was a safe ungrazed location for growing the species. Because of its multiple stems with new ones replacing old, tree-ring analysis is difficult and estimates of age vary wildly. Yews are certainly the longest-lived European species with estimates going up to 5,000 years. While Quantock churchyards do not boast any such monsters, there are a number where the tree is likely to be as old as the church itself. Fig. 1.9 shows a yew at Elworthy in the Brendon foothills where the specimen has grown so large that it is engulfing an eighteenth-century chest grave.

Strand five: Laboratories and refuges

A fifth strand in Quantock history is its curious role both as a place of experiment and as a haven.[16] The earliest known 'scientific' laboratory on the

Fig. 1.9 The church yards around Quantock parish churches are treasure houses of interest. (Left) Bicknoller churchyard. (Right) Ancient yew tree in Elworthy church which has encroached on an eighteenth-century chest tomb.

Quantocks was Combwich, the laboratory of Thomas Chanock, the noted sixteenth-century alchemist who claimed to possess the secret of the philosopher's stone. He was buried at Otterhampton in 1581.

Another laboratory that caught the public gaze was that of Andrew Crosse at Fyne Court, Broomfield. Crosse (1784-1855) was an amateur 'gentleman' scientist who pioneered experiments in the use of electricity. In 1805 the early death of his parents brought him back to the Quantocks when he broke off his legal studies to take over the family estates. His father's friendship with American polymath, Benjamin Franklin, may have started Andrew's interest in lightning. He conducted experiments by criss-crossing the Broomfield estate with over a

linked to a large

nd rows of large

ne) in France on taken from the

Corrigendum

Page 14, line 4. *Insert missing sentence.* 'Other Quantock churches have similar treasures to be found in their memorials, as at St Andrew Old Cleeve.'

nearby Holwell Cavern. During experiments he noted the puzzling emergence of small insects of the genus *Acarus* when his limestone samples were subjected to prolonged electromagnetic currents. Although probably due to biologically contaminated samples, these odd observations were seized on by a local newspaper as a claim that Crosse had created life! To avoid the notoriety that arose, he continued his experiments at Fyne Court in increasing secrecy but continued to be labeled in the press as 'the thunder and lightning man' or 'the wizard of the Quantocks'. In 1814 he met with the poet Percy Bysshe Shelley and his young mistress Mary Wollstonecraft Godwin. Some commentators have linked her subsequent book *Frankenstein* (1818) to visiting Crosse and his electromagnetic laboratory. Locally, Crosse was a keen naturalist, a magistrate and a campaigner for local farmers against falling food prices. Fyne Court was largely destroyed by fire in 1898 but the remaining buildings and the 65-acre estate are now in the hands of the National Trust and can be visited. The nearby parish church of All Saints, Broomfield, contains one of Crosse's laboratory tables and in the churchyard stands an obelisk recalling one of the most extraordinary of Quantock pioneers.

If the Quantocks attracted scientific saints it was also a home to sinners. Most notorious was the Rev Henry James Prince, the unfrocked vicar of Charlynch who in a Weymouth lecture in 1846 declared himself to be the Son Of Man and immortal. He founded at Spaxton the Agapemone (the 'abode of love') and gathered around him there his 'soul brides' (Fig. 1.10). This devoted set of mainly-rich women were fleeced of their fortunes (and a few of their honour) by Prince to maintain a luxurious and hedonistic life style. After Prince's death in 1899 he was succeeded by a New Messiah, Rev Hugh Smith Piggott. The commune attracted worldwide interest and notoriety and letters addressed to 'God, Spaxton,

Fig. 1.10   Contemporary sketch of the Agapemone commune at Spaxton. Source: Bush, 1994 (note 15), 188.

Somerset' continued to be delivered. Even after the second leader died in 1927 the commune lived on with its elderly ladies being much respected for good works in the village. Finally dissolved in 1958, the house and chapel (now minus the high protective wall) remain visible today at Four Forks, Spaxton.

The tranquillity and isolation of the Quantocks attracted regular visitors. Typical was William Temple, Archbishop of Canterbury, who spent his summer holidays in Bicknoller, walking regularly across the Quantocks via Weacombe and Hodders Combe to cream teas in Holford. A small brass plaque on a pew in Bicknoller church records this association over the years 1933-44.

Strand six: Other Quantock muses

The Coleridge-Wordsworth period is rightly celebrated as the star in the Quantocks literary firmament. But its incandescent light is so bright that it hides the area's claims not only to other literary associations, but to wider aspects of the arts through its painters and musicians. Many have found the region a rich source of landscape imagery or of quiet retreat.[17]

One writer who came to the Quantocks late in life was the novelist Evelyn Waugh. He bought Combe Florey House in 1955 when he was in his fifties and lived there until his death in 1966. By then his great novels (such as *Decline and Fall* and *Brideshead Revisited*) were behind him and some thought Waugh a 'literary Garbo' who had come to the Quantocks to be left alone. But he continued to write. His semi-autobiographical *Ordeal of Gilbert Pinfold* (1957), a biography of Ronald Knox, his *Sword of Honour* (1965) trilogy, and his last travel books all date from his Combe Florey period. His son, the critic and commentator Auberon Waugh, took over the house.

Combe Florey's claim to literary fame goes back much further for from 1820 until his death in 1845, the living was held by the Anglican cleric and wit,

Sydney Smith. What his bewildered parishioners thought of a man whose idea of the countryside was that it provided a 'healthy grave' and for whom heaven was 'eating *pâtés-de-foie-gras* to the sound of trumpets' is not known. Few of his Quantock sermons have survived since he was in the habit of throwing them on the fire once they had served their purpose. Parson Holland lived at Over Stowey vicarage in Coleridge's time and left an amusing diary of two decades of Quantock life. A century later, the novelist Phyllis Bottome lived as a child in the same vicarage and records her vivid recollections of the Quantocks:

> The beauty of the waterfalls and streams, the deep red earth, the strong wiry bracken, the low heather hills, the fragrant drenched woods full of moss and ferns: these were the masterpieces of my childhood's world.[18]

While no other Quantock poets of comparable stature to Coleridge and Wordsworth have emerged, the landscape is not entirely bare. Sir Henry Newbolt is best known for patriotic ballad and imperial themes such as 'Drake's drum and other sea songs' (1919). He stayed in his later years at the Aisholt cottage bought by his sister-in-law, Ellie, enjoying himself there 'more than among all the vintages of Italy'. Having found the Quantocks, he wanted to keep them to himself and hoped that 'knowledge of this quiet corner would not be spread too wide'. He would not have welcomed this book.

Some writers had only a fleeting and unsatisfactory contact with the region. Novelist Virginia Woolf wrote to Lytton Strachey from Tarragona, Spain, on September 1st 1912: 'I wonder if you got the card written at the beginning of the tour from the home of Coleridge and Southey?'[19] She had come to the Quantocks on her peripatetic honeymoon, staying at the *Plough* at Holford, 'walking through the mist on the hills' (the weather was terrible) and reading novels in front of the fire. They left for the South of France and Spain within the week. The Quantocks has so far produced no regional novelist of the stature of Exmoor's R.D. Blackmore (*Lorna Doone,* 1869) let alone a Dorset Hardy. Berta Lawrence set one of her novels (*The Nightingale in the Branches*) on a Quantock farm, and a contemporary novelist, Ruth Elwin Harris has published a quartet of historical novels under the title 'Sisters of the Quantock Hills'.

Beyond literature, the story for the other arts is also muted. In painting one Quantock artist, Sarah Biffen, born severely handicapped in East Quantoxhead in 1784 achieved fame and royal approval as a talented miniaturist.[20] The great J. M. W. Turner drew the Quantock coast around Watchet (Fig. 1.11) for his series of engravings in *Picturesque Views of the South Coast of England* and many Quantock churches and great houses were drawn by such artists as William Walter Wheatley: they are housed in the Somerset Heritage Centre. The nearest to a distinctive Quantock 'school' of painters flourished briefly at Halsway Manor in the 1860s when John William North (1842-1924) who was a landscape painter in water

Fig. 1.11 *Over the last two centuries, the Quantock landscape has attracted a wide range of artists and artistic styles. 'Watchet', engraving (above) by Joseph Mallord William Turner (1775–1851) from 'Picturesque Views on the Southern Coast of England', 1820. 'Barford Park' (below), a gouache painting by Jean Rees (1914–2004) c 1960; a coloured reproduction is shown on the cover of this book. Sources. 'Watchet' © Tate Gallery, Image T04397; 'Barford' by kind permission of Mrs Jenny Sharman.*

colour and occasionally oils moved to Somerset and attracted fellow artists to join him in painting scenes from the Quantocks and surrounding countryside. Over the last century, the Quantocks have attracted a range of fine local artists employing a wide range of media and styles to capture its landscape and villages. Rachel Reckitt and Jean Rees (see painting on cover of this book) are among the best. Each September the studios of local artists are open as part of Somerset Arts Week, a feast of colour and technique that is not to be missed.

In music, the Quantocks (unlike the Malverns) has no Elgar. Only in folk music does some of the region's character comes through. Cecil Sharp (1859-1924) originally practiced law in Australia but turned to music and became organist at Adelaide Cathedral.[21] In 1903, while staying with friends in Somerset, he heard a gardener singing 'The seeds of love' while mowing the lawn. This triggered an interest in folk songs which was to dominate the rest of

Sharp's life. Altogether he collected five thousand tunes and lyrics and published his iconic *Folk Songs of Somerset* in five parts between 1904 and 1909. Many of his Somerset songs were collected while cycling from one Quantock village to the next, including the port of Watchet where sea shanties were sung by 'Yankee Jack' whose statue overlooks the marina (see Fig. 7.14).

Strand seven: A crucible for debates

The seventh strand I mention only briefly since we will be looking at this in detail in Chapters 7 and 8. Despite its reputation as a quiet rural backwater for much of its history, the Quantocks in the last century has become a crucible for hot debates on policy issues. These range from local issues (controversy over conifer planting in Quantock combes in the 1920s), through national issues (legitimacy of both deer and fox hunting), to global issues (nuclear power with the building of Hinkley A and B stations and now the proposed building of Hinkley C). Other issues we touch on include branch railways after the Beeching axe, maintaining the heritage of medieval parish churches, the future of the great country houses and estates, and the prospects for villages losing schools, shops, garages and pubs. The Quantocks, despite the beauty of its landscape and the richness of its history, is not cut off from the deep national and global controversies which mark our age.

'QUANTOCK': EMERGENCE OF A NAME

The naming of the land is an important step in recognizing its existence as a geographical entity. The emergence of the 'Quantocks' as a regional concept seems to have depended on three things. First, the appearance of the name on written documents. Second, its location as written on a map. Third, the appearance of a self-conscious 'Quantock' regional literature. We look at each in turn.

How early the name 'Quantock' was used in speech we shall never know. Only in written documents does reliable evidence come to hand and here we have to wait until the Saxon charters of the ninth century.[22] The name first appears around 880 AD as *Cantuctun* and again, two centuries later in Domesday book (1086) in a slightly different form as *Cantoctona* and *Cantetone*. To the etymologists, the name is of mixed origin with the prefix *Cantuc* being Celtic for a 'rim' or 'circle', perhaps suggesting the hills formed (as they do today) a backdrop on the horizon. An alternative rendering is the 'ridge of the Welshmen' where 'Welsh' is used as a general name for Celts. As well as the hills, the term survives in the name of the village of Cannington ('ton' being an Old English word for settlement) on the eastern slopes of the main ridge. Whatever its linguistic origins, we can be sure that the name Quantock was in use at least 1200 years ago and is probably much older.

A second element in recognition is when the area is first shown on maps. County maps of Somerset begin only in the late Tudor period.[23] Thus the 'Quantoke hills' appear in 1610 on John Speed's county map, shown as a diagonal line of fourteen separate 'molehill' symbols running south and east from the sea at Watchet. The main rivers and streams are also shown together with a girdle of villages (each shown by a church symbol). The presence of the county gentry is indicated by the three fenced enclosures around the wooded parkland of Nettlecombe, Stogursey and North Petherton. By the time of Emmanuel Bowen's fine Somerset map of 1760, the form of Quantocks as a continuous hill ridge is very clearly labelled and delineated with fine hachures (see Fig. 1.12).

Detailed maps from this period are generally estate maps drawn for a major landowner to record the precise boundaries of holdings. Somerset historian, Mary Siraut, has found one of the oldest maps in the Somerset Record Office: 'A plot of Quantock belonging to the right honourable the earle of Northumberland, 1609'.[24] Drawn by the London cartographer, Treswell, for the Earl it shows part of the hills in what is now Over Stowey parish. To summarize: by the end of the Saxon period the name 'Quantock' was recorded in documents and by the end of the medieval period the name was firmly on the map.

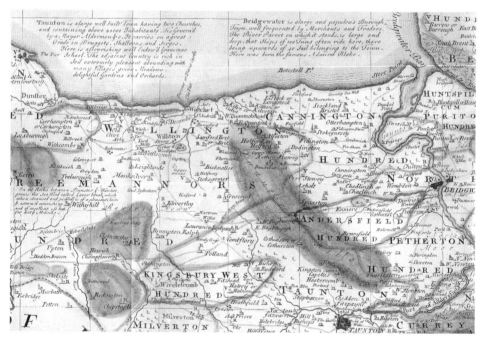

Fig. 1.12 Depiction of the Quantocks on an eighteenth-century map. The steep sides of the hills are shown by hachured shading. Extract from Emmanuel Bowen, Geographer to His Majesty, An Improved Map of the County of Somerset divided into Hundreds, *published c 1760 and dedicated to the Lord Lieutenant of the County, Earl Paulet. Source: Bristol Evening Post reproduction, 1972.*

   The third element in establishing a clear regional identity, a distinctive literature, comes much later. Books specifically concerned with the Quantocks and
with the word appearing in the title seem to be a late Victorian fashion. The long
duration of many Quantock incumbencies gave an opportunity for such
writing. The Reverend William Luke Nichols of Holford wrote papers on the
Quantocks for private circulation, published by his brother after his death in an
extended version as *The Quantocks and their Associations* (1891).[25] Another
archetypal Quantock writer was the Reverend William Henry Parr Greswell
(Fig. 1.13). He grew up in the coastal Quantock parish of Kilve where his father
was rector. After a period as a lecturer in classics in South Africa, he returned to
England and held the living at Dodington between 1888 and 1913. A leading
member of the Somerset Archaeological and Natural History Society, he
researched and wrote a flow of scholarly papers and books on his home area. His
first was on *The Land of Quantock* (1903) and his last, which was written in
retirement in Minehead and appeared a few days before his death, was on
Dumnonia and the Valley of the Parrett (1923). ['Dumnonia' was the Iron Age tribal
division of west Somerset and Devon within which the Quantocks lay.]

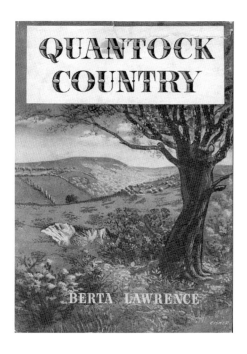

*Fig. 1.13 A distinct regional literature about the Quantocks began to emerge in the late Victorian
period. Reverend William Henry Parr Greswell (1848–1923), vicar of Dodington (upper left)
was one prolific author as was his ecclesiastical colleague W. L. Nichols of Holford (lower left). Sixty
years ago Berta Lawrence provided a definitive regional guide in her Quantock Country (1952).*

Writers about the Quantocks in more modern times have tended to come from educational rather than ecclesiastical backgrounds. Berta Lawrence came to Wembdon near Bridgwater in 1932, when her husband took up a post teaching history at the local grammar school.[26] Both the Lawrence's wrote about the Quantocks: Berta in her *Somerset Journal* (1951) (see Fig. 1.11) and *Quantock Country* (1952) and Jack in *Men and Mining in the Quantocks* (1970). Another schoolmaster, Vincent Waite, wrote a splendid *Portrait of the Quantocks* (1964). Alongside these general accounts of Quantock topography, are the specialist scientific memoirs on the region including Ussher's (1901) study of its geology and Hazel Riley's (2006) outstanding survey of its archaeology.[27]

BEATING THE BOUNDS

I now turn to our third question, one which I've been trying to ignore. How exactly do we define the Quantocks for the purposes of this book? I call this section 'beating the bounds' since it reminds me of the Rogation church ceremony in which priest, churchwardens and congregation process around a parish making sure its boundaries are correctly marked. The Rev Nichols of Holford in his 1891 book took a leisuredly view of the Quantocks and defined it as the area within easy reach of his home at Woodlands (see the map in Fig. 1. 14).

Marking the core of our territory is easy. The long line of the Quantock Hills give a distinctive physiographic marker on the ground and on the map. This identity has been strongly reinforced since 1956 by the area identified as the Quantock Hills Area of Outstanding Natural Beauty. This generally follows the break of slope at the foot of the hills, modified here and there by the line of a road or the need to preserve the integrity of a coastal parish. This legally defined core area covers an area of 38 square miles.

But while this core area is necessary it is not sufficient. If we analyze the AONB then we see that it contains substantial parts of fourteen civil parishes all of which have some part of their land running up onto the hills. Together these parishes cover an area of 61 square miles, half as much again as the defined AONB area. Since Saxon times the parish has been the key organizing unit of English rural life, one embodying both ecclesiastical and civil laws and forming the geographical infrastructure for records and statistics.[28] Most of the historical information about the Quantocks (including the invaluable regional volumes of the Victoria County History) has been and continues to be parish based.[29] Parish boundaries, which needed to be pinned to distinctive landscape features, are often reinforced by markers of hedgebanks. For example, Plate 4 shows the line of beeches south of Crowcombe Gate which marks the Over Stowey – Crowcombe parish boundary.

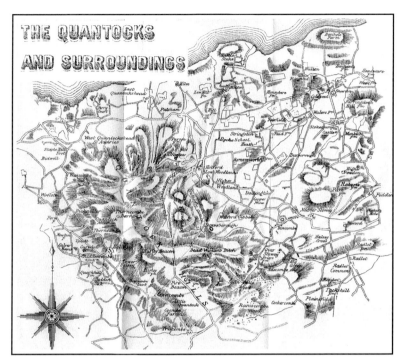

Fig. 1.14 A parochial view of the Quantocks as given in the opening map of W. L. Nichols,
The Quantocks and their Associations, *1891 (note 2). The map covers just the area easily*
accessible to the author's home at Holford.

So if, instead of the AONB, we include all the parishes which have land
running up into the Quantocks, does this solve our boundary problem? Not quite,
for even more distant parishes (such as Stogursey) had historical grazing rights on
the hills and others (Stogumber) once had detached parts of their parish in the
Quantocks. In the end my pragmatic solution (shown in Fig. 1.15) was based on
two premises. First, excluding those areas which were clearly 'non-Quantock': this
eliminated the three bounding towns (Bridgwater, Taunton, Minehead) and three
other distinctive Somerset regions (Exmoor, Taunton Deane, Sedgemoor).[30]
Second, looking at how earlier writers on the Quantocks had drawn their boundaries. Both Lawrence and Waite allowed in their books a generous sweep of land:
from the Brendon Hills in the west almost to the River Parrett in the east, from
the Bristol Channel coast in the north to the vale of Taunton Deane in the south.

My parish solution is slightly more generous than Berta Lawrence's *Quantock*
Country but only marginally so. It includes 35 modern civil parishes in all: a
middle band of fourteen immediately abut the Quantock Hills, a western band
of twelve parishes taking in the foothills of the Brendons but excluding Exmoor
National Park, and an eastern band of nine parishes between the Quantocks and
the Parrett but excluding both Bridgwater and parishes on the line connecting
Bridgwater and Taunton. As thus defined, our Quantocks have a total area of 140

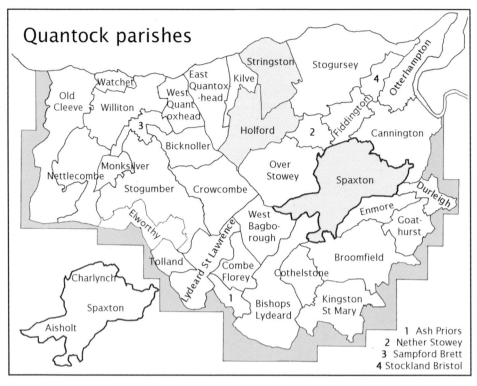

Quantock parishes

1 Ash Priors
2 Nether Stowey
3 Sampford Brett
4 Stockland Bristol

Fig. 1.15 The parish as a regional building block. Civil parishes (35 in all) included in the Quantock region as defined in this book. Several of today's parishes (shaded) are amalgamations of previous ecclesiastical parishes as exemplified by Spaxton (lower left).

square miles. This is over three times greater than the formal AONB definitions but one which I think does better justice to the links between the hills and the surrounding areas.

Before leaving this topic I need to add a 'danger' note. Despite their utility, ubiquity and longevity parishes have drawbacks. First, the present map of civil parishes is not exactly the same as the historical map of ecclesiastical parishes.[31] Over time, parishes with very small populations disappear to become merged with their neighbours. Thus in the last century we have lost Dodington to an expanded Holford, Kilton and Lilstock to Stringston, and Aisholt and Charlynch to Spaxton. At the other extreme, where populations are large and rapidly growing a single parish may be divided. Thus St Decumans parish was divided in 1901 to give separate status to Watchet and Williton and currently Cotford St Luke is separating from Bishops Lydeard. Secondly, parishes are not fixed or watertight containers. At some time in their history, most parishes have had either (a) land outside their borders or (b) enfolded within their bounds land belonging to other parishes. Fig. 1.16 gives examples of both types. Stogumber parish on the edge of the Brendons previously extended over a

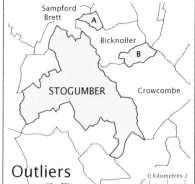

Fig. 1.16 Civil parishes shown on today's maps often have a complex history. (Above) *The line of beech trees on the right of the photo mark an ancient boundary between Crowcombe and Over Stowey on the Quantock ridge. Stogumber parish (lower left) once included outlying sections such as Halsway Manor (see Fig. 7.11) which is today part of Crowcombe Parish. Today's Otterhampton parish* (lower right) *once included many 'inliers' of land belonging to the neighbouring parishes of Cannington and Stockland Bristol. Sources: Dunning, 1985, 176 and Dunning, 1992 (note 29), 104.*

much wider area. On the 1840 map it contains 'inliers', two small parcels of land that belong to Monksilver parish and a third that belongs to Sampford Brett parish. It also has two 'outliers' on the edge of the Quantock Hills at Weacombe and Halsway. Even more complex is the case of Otterhampton parish. Here the map for 1838 shows a fine mosaic of fields with small parcels 'belonging' to neighbouring Cannington and Stockland Bristol parishes.

WRITING ABOUT REGIONS

Once our region's boundaries have been drawn, how do we organize its descriptions? Study of the shelf of volumes in my study that attempt to write about a region show that there are many templates to follow.[32] Both the Lawrence and Waite studies divide the Quantocks into geographical areas but the approach I've followed here is a biographical one, stressing the evolution of the region over time as a narrative.

We start with the far reaches of geological time (Chapter 2) and show the sequence of events which laid down the rocks which make up the Quantock hills and valleys and the varied processes that shaped and reshaped them. Once this physical stage is set, the next five chapters trace the human drama that is played out here. Chapter 3 introduces the first of the *dramatis personae* that creep or strut onto the Quantock scene and over millennia shape its landscape; it reaches back to the last Ice Age with Paleozoic man and ends around 1,000 AD with the Norman Conquest. Chapter 4 covers the long medieval period stretching from the Norman invasion through to the middle of the sixteenth century. It sees the setting out of the pattern of villages and hamlets, of churches and farmsteads, that we see today. Chapter 5 runs from 1550 well into the eighteenth century, from a period of uncertainty in the late Tudor period, to the creation of the great Quantock estates.

The next two chapters bring us to modern times. Chapter 6 describes the later Georgian and Victorian period from around 1750 to 1900: a century and a half of rapid change with the coming of the railways, the re-shaping of Quantock churches, new industries, the rise and fall of agriculture and the farm population dependent on it. Chapter 7 on the twentieth century brings the Quantocks into our own times: the local impact of two world wars, tourism, and the arrival of nuclear power on this rural backwater. In the final chapter (Chapter 8) we stand at the start of a new century and a new millennia and try to look forward to the Quantocks that is emerging around us today.

Each of the six historical chapters covers a different length of time: over 400 million years in Chapter 2, ten thousand in Chapter 3, then 400, 200, 150, and finally 100 years in Chapter 7. The hands of the clock abruptly slow down as we get nearer to the present reflecting the increasing amount of information as we move from the Quantock's deep and largely unknown past to its recent, well-recorded present. What remains constant over the chapters is the attempt to capture the historical processes which are shaping each period and to identify the legacy they have left in today's landscape, always emphasizing those which a visitor can still see today.

Two

THE LIE OF THE LAND

High up on the Quantocks you feel as though you are standing on
an island and, geologically speaking, you are.

Vincent Waite, *Portrait of the Quantocks* (1964).[1]

A ready way to see the shape of Quantock Country is to take the forest road
from Plainsfield up through Cockercombe, park at Triscombe Stone, and walk
past the old beeches up to the region's highest point at Wills Neck. To the north
the whaleback of the hill country rolls away towards Beacon Hill, hiding the
narrow coastal strip where the hills drop steeply down to the Bristol Channel.
On a clear day the coast of South Wales with the Brecon Beacons in the far
distance can just be seen. To the east, the hills drop away in a series of narrow
wooded valleys (locally called 'combes') towards the course of the River Parrett
as it meanders across the Somerset Levels, hemmed in by the low ridge of the
Polden Hills with Glastonbury Tor at its southern end. The pale line of the
Mendip Hills forms the far horizon.

To the south, the view is more curtailed as the main hill ridge widens out into
a series of lower hills with Lydeard Hill partly blocking the view of Cothelstone.
But glimpses of the rich vale of Taunton Deane with its county town and the
Blackdown Hills as its southern border can just be seen. To the west is the best
sight all. The land drops sharply down into the long, village-studded valley
which runs between Bishops Lydeard and the coastal port of Watchet. Beyond
lie the Brendon Hills rising up to the main ridge of Exmoor behind. On the
right are glimpses of the narrow coastal plain running towards Dunster and
Minehead with North Hill plunging sharply into the sea.

Like a piece of music, the Quantock landscape can be enjoyed at several
levels. Simply, for the background pleasure it gives. Or, we can listen a little more
closely, try and pick out the different instruments that create its sounds, identify
its musical structure, its harmonies and repeating themes. The purpose of this
chapter is just that. We try and understand why the lie of the land is as it is.

Why are the hills there? Why is there a straight steep scarp on the western edge of the Quantocks but indenting combes on the gentler east? Why are not the Quantock Hills simply part of Exmoor and what caused the deep valley that today lies between them? When was the terrain shaped and why do we think it once lay under tropical seas, or rose up as a desert mountain range, or shivered on the edge of glaciers? I hope you'll persevere with this chapter for learning to 'read' a landscape, just like reading music, will bring added pleasure. But, if not, just skip to Chapter 3 and begin with the human story.

THE MAKING OF THE QUANTOCKS

In the first half of this chapter we trace the ways in which the Quantocks were shaped. To do this, we have to go back 400 million years to the start of what geologists call the 'Devonian' period.[2] Since such huge time periods are hard to measure against our brief lifespans, you may find it easier to think of this time as a single geological day, starting at midnight. We can then divide this day into four distinct geological periods or 'movements' (to retain our musical metaphor). The first movement is a slow one and one of the longest, from midnight right through daybreak and into mid morning. During it the sediments that make up the Quantock hardcore rocks were slowly accumulated. This quiet period ended with a bang in a late-morning storm of a mountain-building period. Then followed a gentler third movement, lasting through the afternoon and on into early evening, in which the softer sediments that today fill the lowlands around the hills were laid down. Finally, in late evening (65 million years ago) we start a quiet fourth movement, a 'dark age' when so much that had been built in the two previous periods was worn away by erosion to reveal – in subdued form – the old 'fossil' landscape below. This phase ended, at seven minutes to midnight on our geological clock, with the Quantock region covered with snowfields and local ice caps in winter and surrounded in glacial lakes in summer. We take each of the four phases in turn.

Phase I: Laying down the Devonian bedrocks

Rocks of Devonian age underly the whole of the Quantock region. These ancient sedimentary rocks, estimated to be over half a mile in thickness, started to be laid down just over 400 million years ago. As Fig. 2.1 shows, today these 'old red sandstones' are exposed over roughly half of the region, outcropping to form the Quantock Hills themselves and that eastern edge of Exmoor that forms the Brendon Hills.[3]

From north to south the sequence of Devonian rocks gets younger in age. So we can draw a useful distinction both in geological age and in topography between the northern (older) and southern (younger) parts of the Quantock

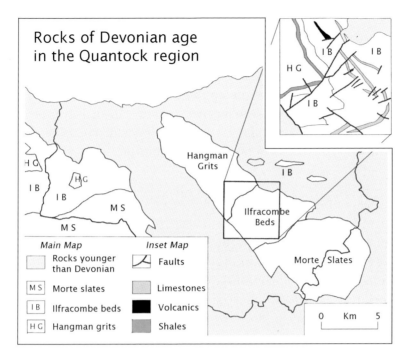

Fig. 2.1 The oldest, hardest and highest rocks of the region which make up the Quantock and Brendon Hills are of Devonian age. This map shows the broad geological divisions within the Devonian sediments and (inset map) the detailed structure of the central part of the Quantocks. Sources: See notes 2 and 3.

Hills. The oldest rocks in the Quantocks are the 'Lynton' slates (the names, like faded Victorian postcards, referring to those parts of the north Devon coast where they were first studied by nineteenth-century geologists). These deposits form the core of Exmoor and extend east to form the base of the Quantocks. They were laid down in shallow seas and comprised mainly slates and siltstones.

The northern and higher part of the Quantock ridge from the seaward end as far south as Wills Neck are formed by the highly erosion-resistant Hangman Grits. These were formed as coastal plain deposit by large alluvial fans on the southern edge of a continental mass extending north through present-day Wales. Like the other Devonian rocks they were affected by deep burial as the accumulation of thick deposits caused the earth's surface to sag and further modified by later mountain-building stresses. The Hangmans consist of fine- to medium-grained quartzitic sandstones, their purple, grey and green colours reminiscent of a bad bruise. Individual beds vary considerably in thickness and interbedding siltstone and slate are more common towards the southern contact with the Ilfracombe beds.

The southern part of the Quantock Hills are lower and more gently sloping with only Cothelstone (1,080 feet) standing out against the horizon. Again, they are forged from sediments of the Devonian period but these are younger and vary in character with distance away from their junction with the Hangmans towards the southeast. First come a band of shales and slates (the Ilfracombe beds), shot through with occasional limestone beds whose fossil corals suggest they were formed as reefs under warm-water conditions. Then come a band of dark-coloured silty slates (the Morte slates) again laid down in marine conditions and compressed by deep burial. Finally, a band of red, purple and green sandstones (the Pickwell series) laid down on the edge of the continent as deltas and in lagoons.

Before leaving this period, we need to take note of a small and isolated hill that lies to the east of the main Quantock Range. Cannington Park (260 feet) is made up of a well-bedded dark grey limestone. It was deposited as a sediment in shallow, warm water with chemically-precipitated lime muds, corals and crinoids (starfish-like creatures) in the Carboniferous age 360 million years ago when this part of Britain lay in the tropical zone. The hill poses a conundrum since it lies separated by some fifteen miles from the nearest rocks of similar age, located in central Devon to the west and Somerset's Mendip Hills to the east. To understand how it came to be here means we have now to turn to the great tectonic forces that came at the end of the first phase period and rearranged the Devonian (and Carboniferous) furniture – the Variscan storm.

Phase 2: The Variscan storm

About 300 million years ago at the end of the Carboniferous there occurred the second of the great mountain-building cycles that have reshaped the Earth's crust at three stages in its history. This one was called the 'Variscan' cycle after the district of Germany where it was first studied in the 1880s.[4] It occurred in the 'late morning' of our Quantock day and although lasting less than one hour on the same clock had immense consequences. It was thought to be caused by sustained northward movement of one of the Earth's tectonic plates and created mountain ranges from the Appalachians of North America right across through middle Europe to the high plateaux of Turkey. In the Quantock region, the Devonian marine sediments laid down in Phase 1 were subjected to northwards pressure along the line of the now Bristol Channel pressing them up against an old continental block, the present Wales. This produced an almost continuous east-west line of thrusting, over-thrusting, and even over-folding, where sediments were pushed up onto and over each other.

This results of these pressures are shown in Fig. 2.2. This draws an west-to-east cross-section from the Brendons across the Quantock ridge to the central Somerset basin. It shows how the Quantock sediments were first forced up into an asymmetric arch (a steep limb on the west, a gentler one on the east) before tension and compression broke the sediments into tilted blocks that behaved like

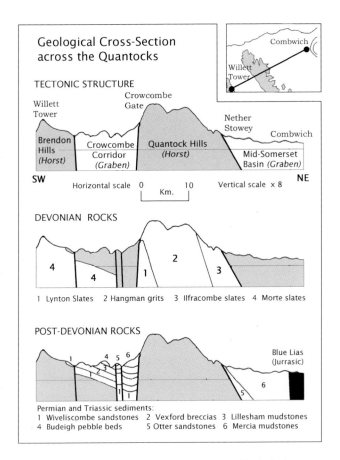

Fig. 2.2 Cross-section across the Quantock Hills to show the block-faulting structure. The section runs from Willett Tower (in the eastern Brendons) to Combwich (on the western edge of the mid-Somerset basin) to show the block-faulting structure. Note the strong vertical exaggeration. Source: Redrawn from Edmond & Williams, 1985 (note 3).

badly-cracked crazy paving. Some blocks like the eastern Brendons and the Quantocks were forced upwards to form raised blocks (the geological term is 'horsts' from the German Rhineland in which they were first described). Other blocks, such as the corridor between Bishops Lydeard and Williton and the Somerset Levels were forced down to form depressed basins ('grabens'). In this scene, the Quantocks stand out like an upthrust island with fault-bounded basins around it on all sides. This horst–and–graben landscape extended west into Exmoor with North Hill and Grabbist as horsts and Porlock vale as a graben. The classic examples of such landforms today are in the high plateaux of the south-west United States.

The original landscape must then have been very much more rugged with a high Quantock mountain ridge standing out above much deeper surrounding basins. Just how rugged we don't know but the Devonian floor between the

Quantocks and the Brendons is thought to go down to 800 feet and the Somerset basin to the east still lower. The amount of vertical movements along the faults can only be roughly estimated but displacements of up to 2,000 feet are thought to occur. Only major faults are shown in this diagram and a distinction can be made between these boundary faults that generally mark a sharp division between the Devonian and later rocks, and a myriad of minor faults within the main formations..

Phase 3: Infilling the lowland basins

The third stage in forming the Quantock terrain was the filling in of the lowland basins that flank the hills. This process began in the mid-afternoon of our 'Quantock day' and we can trace it through into early evening. The infill material was of two different sorts from two different geological periods (see Fig. 2.3).

First, came continental material worn down from the Quantock and Exmoor mountains during the arid conditions of the Permo-Triassic period up to 300 million years ago. These 'New Red' rocks which filled the basins were formed under generally continental and arid conditions. At this stage the Quantock landscape would have looked like the desert 'basin-and-range' part of the South-west United States so beloved as a background in Hollywood cowboy movies. Today's soft combes would then have looked like sharp-edged Arizonan arroyos or Saharan wadis. In these conditions great screes formed around the hills with coarse debris being swept from the barren uplands by occasional, very

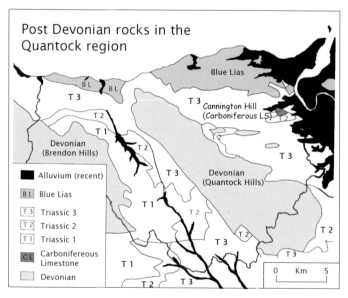

Fig. 2.3 The rocks surrounding the main Quantock ridge are post-Devonian in age. The map shows the main divisions which are Permo-Triassic, Carboniferous and Jurassic in age. Recent alluvial sediments also shown. Sources: See notes 2 and 3.

intense storms. In the centre of the basins, the finer material would form sand dunes, and the still finer material clays and marls. Ephemeral lakes (our small-scale versions of Utah's Great Salt Lake) would dry out to give areas of calcium carbonate accumulation. As the sediments accumulated to fill one basin, so the later deposits would overspill and coalesce from one previously isolated basin to another as the lowland areas filled with debris from the surrounding mountains.

Second, came marine deposits from the Liassic seas of the Jurassic period up to 200 million years ago. A landscape of lakes and desert flats was replaced by one of shallow seas followed by a more general marine transgression. As Fig, 2.3 shows, the Blue Lias rocks of the period lie to the north of the Quantocks extending east along the coast from Blue Anchor deep into Somerset with a general thickness of around 600 feet. The strata are strongly bedded with shales, mudstones and limestones alternating in a succession of sedimentation cycles. As on the Dorset coast, the shales are locally bituminous and potentially oil bearing.

It is easier to study the sediments from this secondary era since many formations are exposed along the cliffed coastline. At low tide, the cliffs and foreshore at Kilve give magnificent exposures of Blue Lias of Lower Jurassic Age (Plate 6A). The map-like view of beach from the cliff path shows sweeps of folding and faulting of both compression and extension types while the formations can be traced in cross-section on the cliff faces. The Kilve and Lilstock area is rich in fossils, particularly ammonites, reflecting the varied fauna of the species-rich Liassic seas. Plate 6B shows a typical ammonite set in a farm wall on the footpath

Fig. 2.4 One of the only stones in the Quantocks capable of fine carving is soft alabaster rock exposed on the cliffs between Watchet and Blue Anchor. Here in the parish church of St Mary the Virgin, Nettlecombe, it is used for the intricately-carved octagonal font, showing the sacraments. The last rites are being given in the panel shown.

to East Quantoxhead church. Study of the cliffs at both Blue Anchor and Watchet are rewarding. At the former, the cliffs extending from the eastern end of the extensive sea wall show red mudstones of the Triassic period. Further along are exposures of the famous evaporates which were created in dried-up lake beds under extreme desert conditions. They form masses and veins of pink, nodular gypsum along the cracks and fault planes (see Fig. 2.4).

Phase 4: Exhuming the fossil landscapes

The fourth stage in forming the Quantock terrain was the progressive 'exhumation' of the old Variscan landscape to give the much subdued replica we see around us today. This process began in the early evening of our 'Quantock day' and continued to midnight; indeed, erosion continues today. As in the case of Phase 3, we can trace it through two distinct phases and we take each in turn.

There are long periods in the geological history of the Quantocks about which very little is known. One such 'dark age' runs from the last Jurassic sediments laid down in the area (more than 135 million years ago) to the very recent quaternary sediments (laid down within the last two million years). Over that vast time period we have no local geological deposits to study. The Cretaceous sea which saw the laying down of the chalk deposits that form the characteristic downland scenery of the south and east of England appears not to have extended this far west. Or, if it did, it either left no deposits or any laid down were worn away by later erosion. For when the Creatceous seas dried out about 65 million years ago, newly created land in the west slowly rose leaving only part of south-east England under water.

Much of the subsequent history of the period must have been the reduction of that land mass, stripping away the newer and softer sediments to reveal the fossil structures of the Devonian, Triassic and Liassic landscapes lying beneath. The dominant process in that erosion was accomplished by the great rivers whose alignments (not, of course, their actual channels) some scholars see traces of today. Thus the line of the River Tone is seen as a remnant from a major river system that once drained eastwards across southern England towards what is now the Thames basin and the adjacent parts of the North Sea. With the opening of the Bristol Channel in the late Tertiary the Tone was eventually 'beheaded' by the northward flowing River Parrett.

How far marine erosion played any part in the exhumation process is a subject of debate. One observer, sees the Quantocks emerging from isolated island, through archipelago, to continuous ridge as sea levels fell over a twenty-million year period during the late Tertiary period (see Fig. 2.5).[5] The reconstruction depends on map-contour evidence with flat areas, some of which cut across highly folded and varied rock types, interpreted as evidence of marine erosion where the sea retained its level for long periods. Conversely, breaks of

Emergence of the Quantock ridge in the Teriary period

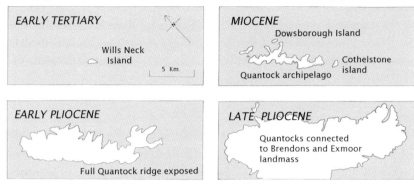

EARLY TERTIARY

Wills Neck
Island

5 Km

MIOCENE

Dowsborough Island

Quantock archipelago

Cothelstone
island

EARLY PLIOCENE

Full Quantock ridge exposed

LATE PLIOCENE

Quantocks connected
to Brendons and Exmoor
landmass

Fig. 2.5 The emergence of the Quantock ridge during the late Tertiary period according to W. G. V. Balchin (1952). (Above) Map of four stages of sea-level retreat leaving old shorelines planed across different lithologies. (Below) The highest point on the main ridge of the Quantocks is Wills Neck at 1,260 feet. It is marked by a round barrow (see also Fig. 3.3) on which a trigonometric survey pillar was built by the Ordnance Survey in 1936 as part of the their nationwide re-triangulation programme. Source: Map redrawn from Balchin, 1952 (note 5).

slope are seen as evidence of degraded cliff lines for a once higher sea level. Fragments of the surfaces at similar heights are aligned and estimates of former coastlines drawn in.

Finale: The Quantocks in the Ice Age

At the very end of the fourth period with just seven minutes left on the Quantock clock, came the succession of ice ages and inter-glacials that we think of collectively as an Ice Age. This is the period of two million years through which we are living now. Some scientists have thought that at its peak extent (roughly half a million years ago) glaciers might have swept across south-west

England. But there is no local evidence for the Quantocks or Exmoor for this. Most accounts place West Somerset just to the south of the main ice sheets at their most southerly extent.[6] So we have to imagine a continuous ice sheet, much like that covering Greenland today, stretching south across the British Isles to the line of the present Bristol Channel. Snowfields and even local ice caps might be present on Exmoor, the Quantocks and the Mendips though these would shrink seasonally.

In front of the main ice sheet, the summer melt waters from the glaciers ponded to form great lakes. Thus the damming of the Bristol Channel by ice led to the forming of a huge lake (Lake Maw) filling the Somerset Levels, lapping against the high ground of the Somerset uplands, and possibly overspilling south near Chard towards the English Channel. Such 'spillways' were an important feature of the ice-sheet edge. Both ice and lakes would have disrupted pre-existing streams and Fig. 2.6 shows how the Holford stream was diverted from its orginal course (A) to the coast at Stolford. When that earlier course was blocked, the stream was diverted to (B) and eventually to its present entrenched northerly route to the coast near Kilve (C).[7] Many of the valleys that run down from the Quantocks seem large for their present streams and may well have been greatly enlarged by carrying floodwater from melting ice and snow.

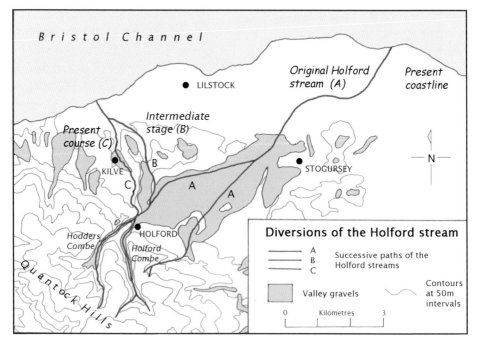

Fig. 2.6 Diversion of the lower course of the Holford-Hodder stream in Quaternary times after it debouches onto the lowlands from its Quantock Hills catchment. A, B and C mark three different pathways taken by the stream. Source: Penning Rowsell, 1974 (note 7).

Whatever the precise limits of the northerly ice sheets during the mid Quaternary, the Quantock's climate was very severe for the next 100,000 years. The closest climatic comparison is with the tundra of northern Siberia, snow covered in winter, bare ground with lichens and mosses in summer. The effects of this severe episode can be seen today. Frost-shattered material from the summits crept downslope through a freeze-and-thaw process, creating great aprons of material that lie on the flanks of hills and clog many of the existing combes.[8] Such valley debris is being eroded by the steams today. It is difficult to see these frost-shattered deposits in the hills themselves except where floods may expose stream banks. But along the northern coast, as at Doniford Bay east of Watchet, the overlying valley gravels descend to beach level. These show both infilled valleys and evidence of the effect of freeze-thaw patterning.

Processes of landscape change continue today in what is probably just the most recent inter-glacial period. The changing course of the River Parrett which forms the eastern boundary of our region illustrates the point. Archaeological evidence from the Roman period (see Chapter 3) confirms that the river then had a different line. A major meander sweep brought the river to Crandon Bridge on the edge of the Poldens a mile east of its present course. More recent map evidence (see Fig. 2.7) shows changes over a forty-year period in the mouth of the river.[9] The coast continues to change today with experiments with marked pebbles showing an eastward movement of shingle (up to two miles in a decade) along the low coast from Hinkley Point towards Stert Point.[10] The best location to see these processes at work is to visit Wall Common near Steart where old shingle beaches show the tangled history of the coast with post-glacial rises in sea level attested by the submerged forests found

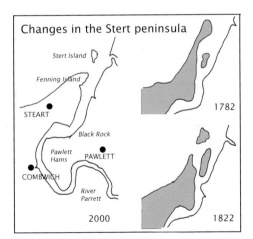

Fig. 2.7 Changes in lower course of the River Parrett in recent historical times. The present position (left) is compared with that shown on maps forty years apart, in 1782 and 1822 (right). Source: Harley & Dunning, 1981 (note 9).

at lower beach levels at nearby Stolford. The area is now part of the Bridgwater Bay National Nature Reserve discussed in Chapter 8.[11]

Stream erosion continues today, particularly when there are extreme storms. Even on the tectonic front, small movements continue along the Quantock faults with the last major tremors recorded as small earthquakes in the years 1276, 1682 and 1839.[12] Like the rest of southern Britain, this part of the Earth's crust is still adjusting to the 'unloading' of the huge weight of the ice sheets.

THE GEOLOGICAL LEGACY

The geological history of the Quantocks is not just of antiquarian interest. The four great movements have left a legacy which, for good or ill, continues to influence us today. It is this inheritance – the scenery of hills and combes, mineral riches and poverty, rich soils and poor – which forms the essential stage on which all the acts of the human drama which follows (in Chapters 3 to 8) are played out.

Terrain: structure and scenery

The lie of the Quantock land is a direct legacy of its geological history. Fig. 2.8 shows the iconic core of the Quantock region, the diagonal backbone ridge of the Quantock Hills. These rise to a height of over 1,100 feet at several points and trend NW-SE for twelve miles, narrow in the north at three miles across but flaring out in the south to a width of five miles. At the largest scale, the link between the highest land and the distribution of Devonian rocks on the geological map (Fig. 2.1) is self-evident. The Old Red Sandstones are harder and more resistant to erosion than the younger sediments around them. But if we recall that Devonian rocks underly *all* of our area then this cannot be the whole story. The present elevation of the Quantock Hills can only be explained by adding in the tectonic forces which pushed them up in the Variscan period and pushed the lowlands down at the same time.

The flexing of those sediments into an asymmetric arch with the great boundary fault (the Cothelstone fault) on the west, helps to explain the contrast by the two flanks of the Quantock Hills: short, steep combes to the west of the watershed; long, branching, and less steep combes to the east (Fig. 2.9). Within the Hangmans, the effects on scenery of small variations in sediments can readily be traced. The thick Trentishoe Grits form the base and coincide with the highest part of the hills. Above these Rawn's Shales contain more clayey material and have commonly been sought out and followed by streams such as Holford Combe whose north-south alignment also reflects local faulting.

As with the Devonian, small variations in the make-up of the younger sediments of Permo-Triassic age are reflected in topography of the lowland

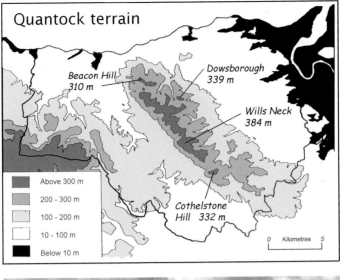

Fig. 2.8 The basic shape of Quantock terrain. Photograph (below) shows a view northwest from Cothelstone Beacon showing the steep western face of the hills, the intervening Crowcombe trough, and the Brendon Hills rising towards Exmoor.

basins. Such contrasts are best seen in the Bishops Lydeard to Watchet basin west of the Quantock Hills. Rocks that were laid down as screes and breccias form today a distinct scarp facing towards the Brendons. Those formed from pebble accumulations were later cemented together by lime and iron and now give the distinctive flat-topped plateau rising to over 200 feet west of Crowcombe. In contrast, softer rocks derived from marls and muds form broad plains at lower elevations. East of the Quantocks, the same triple topographic pattern of scarp, plateau and plain is repeated but since the basin is here so much broader the landform changes are less abrupt.

At Pawlett Hill, the diagonal line of the Polden Hills swings west to reappear as a line of low hills running roughly parallel to the coast between Stockland

Quantock combes

Smiths Combe

Weacombe

Holford Combes

Crowcombe combe

Rams- combe

Land over 600 ft

Buncombe

`. . .` Watershed

Land over 600 ft

Fig. 2.9 Stream dissection of the Quantock ridge. (Left) Map showing asymmetry of the water-shed on the tilted block. Contrasting forms of the combes eroded in Hangman Grits on the eastern and western side of the northern Quantocks are shown by the short steep combe at Weacombe (upper right) contrasted with the longer, more gently sloping and branching combes of the Holford-Hodder stream on the western side (lower right).

Bristol and Watchet. Here the dip of the Blue Lias strata is consistently to the north, so the escarpment faces south with the ridges running east and west. Although once continuous, later tectonic activity caused tilting and minor faulting so that the original escarpment is now incomplete and broken and, like a curtain or wallpaper pattern, has its key features repeated several times.

Building stones

The Quantocks have a wide and colourful array of useful building stone though none valuable enough to be exported outside the region.[13] Stone is so heavy and difficult to move that only the very best can stand the costs of transport. So a good rule of thumb in walking the Quantock landscape is to look for evidence of local geology in the humblest stone structures (field walls, gate posts, barns and outbuildings, the foundations and lower walls of old farm houses and churches). The area is riddled with small quarries and scrapes from which such stone was won, most in the immediate backyards of the buildings they were used to construct.

For more ornate use of stone, say in carved window mullions or fine monuments, stone was imported from the great Somerset quarries: warm, golden limestone from Ham Hill near Yeovil, the white-yellow oolitic limestone from Doulting near Wells, and the cream-coloured oolitic Bath stone from Dundry. In these cases, the value of the pre-cut stone compensated for high transport costs and it was brought into the region via coastal ports such as Watchet, Combwich and Bridgwater and then moved on by river and stream to get as near the building site as possible.[14]

The hardest of the local stones, the Hangman Grits, were generally too difficult to work into regular blocks so they tended to be used as rough fieldstones, built into thick church walls (as at Holford) or used for quoins in barns and farm buildings. But this resistance made them useful for roadstone and small roadside quarries (as in the road from Over Stowey up to Deadwoman's Ditch) abound. The younger and softer Ilfracombe beds and Morte slates with marked cleavage lines were used for walling (Plate 6E). Good examples of their use in building can be seen in Broomfield parish church and in the walls and flagstone paths of the Lutyens-Jekyll garden at Hestercombe (see Chapter 7). Rare igneous intrusions within the Devonian also provided Lutyens with building stone (using the Hestercombe diorite) while the greenish-grey Cockercombe tuff (a volcanic ocean floor deposit) was chosen by Lord Taunton in building Quantock Lodge at Over Stowey in the 1850s (see Plate 14B).

After the Devonian, later sedimentary rocks provided a richer range of building stone. The carboniferous limestone makes a durable building stone which can be seen used in the village of Cannington today and the quarry continues to be actively worked for roadstone. Of the variety of Permo-Triassic rocks, the Otter sandstone with its easily-worked red and buff stone was widely used for walling and for building stone, as in the successive rebuildings of Bishops Lydeard church (Plate 8B). The Liassic stones with their pronounced bedding planes and their range of colours from blue-grey to yellow ochre were widely used on the northern plain for walling stone (Plate 6C), floor slabs and tombstones. The medieval church at East Quantoxhead, the adjacent Court House, the tithe barn and complex of farm buildings provides an unforgettable combination of greys, blues and sandy yellows.

One unusual example of a Quantock stone used for fine carving we noted earlier (Fig. 2.4). It is found in the cliffs between Watchet and Blue Anchor. Here lake deposits laid down under the arid conditions of the Permo-Triasic give rise to gypsum which, as alabaster, was used for carving some fine church monuments. The alabaster font at Nettlecombe church is thought to have been carved in the late medieval period. A convenient way to see the full range of building stones from the Quantocks is to stop on the platform of Watchet station (on the West Somerset Railway) where a Jubilee Geological Wall has examples of rocks from the local area.

Mineral and water resources

The Quantock region has a variety of metal ores. Iron working is mentioned at Spaxton in the Domesday survey (see Chapter 4) and was to be critically important on the Brendon Hills (to the west of our region) in the late nineteenth century where it contributed significantly to the growth of the region's largest settlement, Watchet.

Records of copper workings occur first in 1714 at Perry Hill (near West Quantockshead) in the north of the district, but it was Dodington on the eastern edge of the hills that was the main focus of activity.[15] The history of the two copper mining phases from 1786 to 1810 and again from 1817 to 1822 are described in Chapter 6 (see also Plate 6D). Copper ores form part of a suite of minerals (including small traces of lead, silver and even gold) which suggest that such ores have a very old and deep origin in the Earth's surface. Limestone bands seem to have provided passages which allowed minerals in a molten and gaseous state to rise through an overburden of sediments towards the surface. At Dodington, copper ores tended to be concentrated in such limestone veins at the junction of Devonian slates with Otter sandstones and as Fig. 2.10 shows,

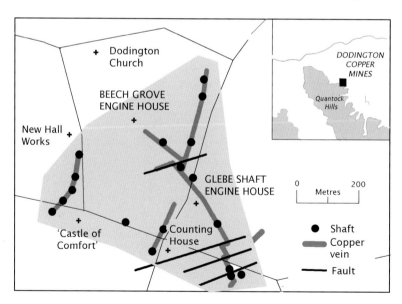

Fig. 2.10 Abandoned copper-mining area near Dodington on the northeastern side of the Quantock Hills. The position of the main copper veins is shown. The history of the mines is discussed in Chapter 6 and for a photograph of a ruined engine house, see Plate 6D. Source: Map based on reconstruction by Mike Jones in Lawrence & Hamilton, 2008 (note 15), 46-49.

mining adits tended to follow a zig-zag path tracking the veins which had been much disrupted by later faulting.

Although the Quantock region went through the Carboniferous period when tropical vegetation laid down the source from which coal measures would be formed, rocks of this age are only exposed in the carboniferous limestone of Cannington Hill. Barytes, a mineral form of barium, occurs in veins within the limestone, has been quarried at Cannington and occurs elsewhere east of the Quantocks. Coal is nowhere found in the region though a trial pit was sunk at Crowcombe in 1753 but without success.

The Liassic seas laid down deposits that contained oil-rich shales and triggered a short-lived mining boom in the 1920s (see Chapter 7). Blue Lias rocks also provided a rich source of surface limestones which could be worked through shallow quarries for lime burning. Kilns are widely scattered throughout the region, both on the liassic formations and in the narrow limestone bands that occur widely throughout the older rock formations. A typical kiln is shown in Fig. 2.11. Clays and marls on the margins of the area were used for brick making, notably at Combwich and Blue Anchor.[16]

Over the centuries, the most critical Quantock resource has been its rich water resources. Lying squarely across the prevailing south-westerly winds the main Quantock ridge triggers precipitation so that its annual totals run at triple the level of the relative rain-shadow area in its lee. The water trickling down its slopes and accumulating in its sediments have provided springs for village, hamlet and farm water supply and rich meadows for its livestock. The streams rushing down its combes and debouching across its plains provided energy for scores of water mills, powering rural industry for over a millennium. In the last century stream water from the eastern Quantocks has been ponded to form

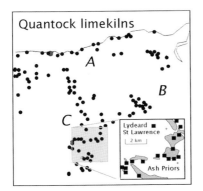

Fig. 2.11 Scores of kilns were built across the region to provide lime for agricultural improvements in the Victorian period. (Left) Map of recorded kilns in the Quantocks with inset map of an area near Lydeard St Lawrence showing the relation of kilns to pebble beds. (Below) An abandoned kiln at Kilve Beach. Source: Prudden, 2001 (note 16), 32-34.

three reservoirs at Ashford, Durleigh and Hawkridge. Surface water tends to shed quickly off the hard Devonian rocks and it is only along fault lines with crushed rocks that these form local aquifers. Where such water does not drain off to the sea in local watercourses, it soaks down into the more permeable of the surrounding secondary rocks. Two important strata for such water storage are rocks of Permo-Triassic age which are either pebbly conglomerates or have open sandy structures (e.g. the Otter Sandstones).

Land quality

A third legacy of the Quantock's geological history comes in terms of its land quality. Each group of settlers will have viewed the land resources slightly differently depending on their culture and technology : a very steep slope provides a different set of problems and potentials if you are approaching it with a stone

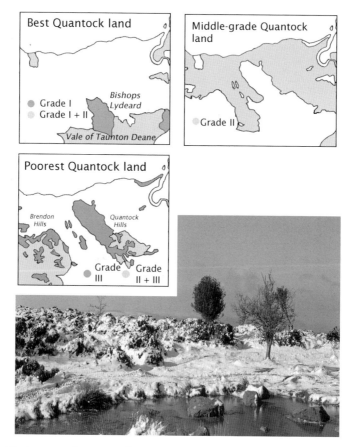

Fig. 2.12 Environmental regions of the Quantocks based on one of several mapping systems developed to attempt to measure the land potential. The distribution of the best, middle grade, and poorest divisions are mapped. The winter photo below shows the poorest land near Bicknoller Post under snow. Source: Maps redrawn from University of Bristol, 1947 (note 17).

Fig. 2.13 Contrasts in land quality in the northern Quantocks. View looking south across the Luttrell estate at East Quantoxhead with cultivated Grade II land (see Fig. 2.12) developed on Liassic bedrock in the foreground. The land rises steadily at the junction with older Devonian bedrock to give the open moorland on Longstone Hill and West Hill on Grade III land in the background.

axe, an Iron Age plough, or a John Deere tractor. Of the various schemes put forward to measure the region's land quality, I've chosen one developed by Bristol University scientists (Fig. 2.12).[17] It weaves together three elements: (1) local terrain, e.g. slope steepness, ease of drainage, liability to flooding; (2) local climate, e.g. exposure, aspect, length of growing season; (3) local soils, e.g. depth, composition, soil chemistry. These different environmental measures are each scored and then combined to give a simple yardstick of Grade I land (high potential), Grade II land (medium potential) and Grade III (poor potential). Since land quality may vary abruptly over short distances, two mixed grades I + II (mainly medium with some good) and II + III (mainly medium with some poor) are introduced for mapping at medium scales.

The map shows the main ridge of the Quantocks standing out as a zone of poor Grade III land with outliers also in the steeper terrain of the eastern Brendons. An example of the junction of Grades II and III land in the northern Quantock Hills is shown in Fig. 2.13. At the other extreme, the main area of good Grade I land is clustered around Bishops Lydeard to the southwest of the hills. There are also small outliers of Grade I land east of the main Quantock ridge around Cannington. For the most part, the remainder of the lowland Quantock country is either Grade II or one of the intermediate grades. These divisions are reminiscent of French *terroir* underlining the essential sub-structure of Quantock regions which appear, time and time again, in its history.

The main shape of the present Quantock landscape is in its rough outline very ancient. Indeed, the basic contrast between upland and lowland was imposed around 250 million years ago and, despite subsequent sedimentary burials, has been exhumed to form the main framework today. Later processes, despite their intrinsic interest, have only bevelled, infilled and moulded features at smaller scales leaving the basic geography little altered. The huge time range allowed both great periods of inactivity and still-stand and yet permitted enormous change in the environment in which deposition and erosional forces were working. Today's temperate Quantock environment is only one phase from a history which has switched from mountain range to offshore lagoons, from desert heat to near-glacial cold, from stable block to tectonic splitting. The Quantock region has at various times during its long history, looked like an Arizona desert, a Great Barrier Reef shelf, or a Spitzbergen tundra. This complex history of land formation has left a legacy which shaped the use of this area when, in the last few seconds of our long Quantock day, the first human actors stepped tentatively onto the Quantock stage.

Three

SETTLING QUANTOCK COUINTRY

The Quantock Hills contain many prehistoric field monuments. Although modest in scale, and not always easy to find in their often remote and beautiful locations, they are well worth seeking out.
Leslie Grinsell, *Prehistoric Sites in Quantock Country* (1991)[1]

One of Leslie Grinsell's 'remote monuments' which I enjoy seeking out is Higher Hare Knap (Plate 7A). To get there I leave the car in the wooded car park by the Bowling Green at Holford and head southwest along a well-marked path rising on the ridge between two combes, Butterfly Combe to the left and Hodders Combe to the right. Within a mile of gentle climbing, the oak woodlands on the two valley sides fall away below and on the ridge I am surrounded by heather and bilberry moorland alternating with swathes of bracken and dotted with the occasional windblown thorn and holly bush. This is classic Coleridge - Wordsworth walking country (which we met in Chapter 1) and there are fine examples of the lichen-clad trees described somewhat soulfully in William's narrative poem, 'The Thorn'. Already, there are fine views in all directions. To the left and right the ridges of the Quantocks encircle around like the arms of a comfortable, well-worn easy chair.

But nearer to hand and just off the main path there is a pile of stones, marked on the map as Higher Hare Knap. The low cairn of stones is only three or four yards across and less than a third as high. Why is it here? Is it recent or old? While we shall never know for sure, it is possible that it dates back four thousand years to the Bronze Age. It may well be part of a ritual memorial landscape: Jane Brayne's evocative painting in Heather Riley's classic book on the archaeology of the Quantocks shows Higher Hare Knap as the site for a Bronze Age funeral pyre.[2] Her vivid reconstruction shows four family groups – men, women and children in arms – converging along the ridge pathway (which I've just walked) heading towards the burning site where the death of a tribal elder is being marked.

The Quantock landscape is full of such mysteries and although we try in this chapter to reconstruct the pattern of Quantock settlement over past millennia, we must acknowledge how little we know with certainty and how much is thoughtful speculation. The sequence I follow in this chapter owes much to the American historian, Frederick Jackson Turner, who in his 'frontier thesis' saw the settlement of the West as a series of human waves rolling over that distinctive environment.[3] Each wave of settlers brought to that environment its own distinctive culture and technology, meeting or being overwhelmed by the challenges and opportunities the new territory had to offer.

In the long, slow history of occupying Quantock country, the chapter identifies four waves. First, a wave of migrant hunter-gatherers who for millennia crept hesitantly into and out of the area in small nomadic bands whenever climate and the richness of nature's bounty allowed. Only when hardwood forests permitted could such foraging groups inhabit larger territories on a semi-permanent basis. Second, a farming frontier from around 4,500 B.C. when some form of permanent settlement was possible. Third, a military occupation from A. D. 43 with the arrival of Rome's imperial legions and the legacy it left. Fourth, the Saxon frontier from around the seventh century which set out the dispersed settlements, many of which were to grow into the villages which persist today. Much of the familiar human landscape which we see in the Quantocks had its origins in this Saxon wave. For each of the four frontier movements we try and identify the kind of environment that was encountered, the way its challenges were met, and the effects it had on the Quantock landscape. We also try to identify sites where some evidence of early presence can be seen today.

WAVE I: NOMADIC HUNTER-GATHERER BANDS

If we use the device of Chapter 2 and try to think of time as a day-long geological clock, then human exploration comes onto the scene only late in the last minute of Quantock evolution. Cave deposits from the nearby Mendip Hills suggest human occupancy might stretch back well across several interglacials, but the broader evidence across western Europe places the first human incursions into this part of southern England at around 70,000 B.C. If we take this conservative figure then, in terms of our Quantock clock, then humans may first have visited the region in the more productive phases and seasons with only fifteen seconds of the day to go. Fixed year-round settlement came from around 4,500 B.C., i.e. with just one second to go on the Quantock geological clock![4]

The challenge of the Quantock environment

As we saw in the last chapter, at the glacial maxima the Quantocks lay just south of the Quaternary ice sheet so would have had conditions which were probably too severe for human occupation: semi–permanent snowfields on the higher land, tundra conditions on the lower slopes, with huge summer lakes drowning the lowest ground. But as conditions improved and ice sheets slowly melted so the ecological zones would have shifted northwards with low scrub and finally trees occupying the formerly barren landscape.

The sequence of ice sheets left a stark legacy among the flora and fauna of southern England. If we take just one element, trees, then in late Tertiary times some 60 million years ago the Quantocks were near the latitude of the present Mediterranean Sea with a rich tree flora. This richness was reduced as the area drifted into higher latitudes until, about one million years ago, the Ice Ages started. Successive waves of ice cleared the country of all trees except a probable refuge area off south-west England (now covered by sea). With the retreat of the last ice sheet some 11,000 years ago, northward colonization of trees from southern Europe proceeded but was brought to a sudden halt about 6,000 years ago when rising sea levels completed the breach between southern England and northern France.[5] So the area which early man explored in the latest post-glacial had a limited tree palette of only 35 species. The extreme story for trees has its parallel in other plant and animal populations.

The story of environmental change over the last 12,000 years is summarized in a highly simplified form in Fig.3.1.[6] A sequence of five main bioclimatic phases (Dryas, Boreal, Atlantic, Sub-Boreal and Sub-Atlantic) is recognized together with approximate trends in vegetation, sea levels, warmth and the

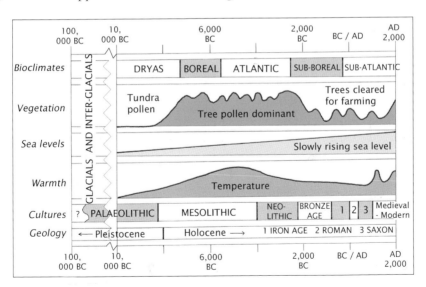

Fig. 3.1 Main environmental and archaeological divisions over the last twelve thousand years. Generalized patterns for bioclimatic, vegetation, sea levels, warmth, cultures and geology are shown. On the left the period of glacial and inter-glacials back to 100,000 BC are shown. Source: Drawn from multiple sources (see note 6).

human cultures that had to cope with these environments. The first bioclimatic phase, the Dryas, was named after *Dryas octopetala*, a dwarf eight-petalled herbaceous plant of the rose family (today sometimes grown by gardeners as an Alpine). Its pollen is a fossil indicator of tundra conditions. At that time the climate was severely sub-Arctic with large barren areas, and sedges, grasses, mosses, lichens, juniper, and dwarf birch. Pollen analysis (much influenced by early Scandinavian research but locally spurred on by the work of Harry Godwin and his associates on the Somerset levels) is the main source of evidence for these changes. For the Quantocks *per se* local evidence is limited to the submerged forests found north of the present coastline off Stolford. These form part of a series of sites around the shores of the Severn estuary where stumps of trees (including oak, ash, willow) can be observed in the offshore tidal zone. Where tree-ring and radio-carbon dating has been attempted, they suggest dates between 6,000 and 4,000 B.C. with evidence of peat formation (which may have preserved the tree remains) and of human occupation of Mesolithic age.

Early explorers: the Palaeolithic hunter-gatherers

Evidence across Europe suggests that as the ice sheets stagnated and melted and the sub-arctic tundra conditions ameliorated, so potential food supplies (both plant and animal) grew until they could sustain small and roving bands of human hunters and gatherers. For millennia, these incursions of human populations from the warmer south were temporary. They probably followed the longer cycles of warming and cooling and the shorter cycles of the seasons. As the floral and faunal zones shifted so *Homo sapiens* migrated with them. As herds of deer or bison moved north, so the hunters followed; as conditions became more severe the animals had to move south and the hunters moved with them.

We can reconstruct likely conditions in two different ways. First, by studying the local distribution of archaeological finds. We know of the presence of the early hunters through the record of stone tools which they left behind them. For Quantock country the richest areas for stone-age finds have been the river and coastal gravels where the Doniford brook nears the sea (Fig. 3.2). While this concentration may partly reflect the assiduity of local Watchet archaeologists, it also fits in with the ideas of Berkeley geographer, Carl Sauer, who argued that movements of early man along river and coastline corridors was critical as both freshwater and saltwater provided a wider range of year-round foods (including fish, molluscs and seaweeds) than land resources.[7] The winter months provided the great survival hurdle for stone-age peoples, a challenge which continued into at least medieval times. Unlike the cave-rich Mendips, the Quantocks afforded few winter shelter sites (Holwell cavern at Merridge being an exception). We know from the river gravels around Doniford that flint tools (oval, pear shaped implements and pointed hand axes) were found close to the teeth and

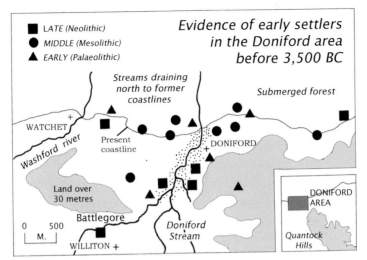

Fig. 3.2 *Evidence of early stone-age peoples in the Doniford area of the northern Quantocks before 3,500 BC. Note that the position of the fluctuating sea-level would then have lain north of the present coastline. (Inset) Location of the Doniford area in relation to the Quantock Hills. Sources: Map based on Grinsell, 1991, and Riley, 2006 (notes 1 and 2).*

tusks of mammoths suggesting the presence of a Palaeolithic hunting culture.[8]

A second approach to reconstruction is through studying anthropological accounts of migrant tribes facing extreme environmental conditions in our own historical times. The complex hunting strategies and migration behaviour of tribes on the tundra fringe in northern Canada or Siberia (or even in northern Japan or the desert-fringe in Australia) give insights into how human groups can survive and thrive under these challenges. We can be sure that early groups were sensitive to the full range of different Quantock environments and squeezed the maximum sustainable yield (both animal and vegetable) from them.

But numbers must have been tiny and for century-long periods the Quantocks may well have been empty or visited rarely. One estimate of England's total population in 10,000 B.C. is 2,000 of which (assuming similar densities across the land) the Quantock share would have been just five souls! Very occasional visits by small roving bands of 25 or so seems much more plausible.

Opening up the woods: the Mesolithic peoples

Stone-using peoples (the *–lithic* peoples from the Greek word for 'stone') have conventionally been divided into three time groups by prefixing with the Greek words for old, middle and new as the Palaeolthic, Mesolithic and Neolithic peoples. The duration of each culture varied hugely, with the time ratios of roughly >40 : 2 :1 respectively. By about 8000 B.C. major changes started to occur in the Quantock environment. By then warming temperatures had seen most of the ice disappear from the British Isles and the sparse tundra vegetation that had dominated in the later Dryas period was succeeded by a scrub of low bushes, scattered trees, and eventually forests. Over the next 2.5 millenia the period was termed the Boreal phase, after the great circum-polar forests of the northern hemisphere. It was marked by a continental climate with rapidly rising temperatures. Pollen records suggest that aspen, birch and Scots pine were slowly replaced by extensive pine and hazel forests as a warmer, more continental climate began to dominate. They also show the first appearance of elm, oak, lime, and alder with a steady transition to an elm and oak dominance. There was a drop in the percentage of herb pollen as once open areas were invaded by the forest community. With deglaciation came rising sea levels with southern Britain cut off from the continent by about 6000 B. C.

Where human sites are known they continue to suggest seasonal occupation with hunting animals and fishing supplemented by harvesting of shellfish and seasonally-available fruits and nuts. The tools found in the archaeological record around Doniford (Fig. 1.2) are now more sophisticated with bone harpoons and a subtle range of flint tools from axes through to scrapers and arrowheads. By now the coastline had changed again and lay a mile or so further out into the Severn estuary so that coastal Mesolithic sites are now likely to be covered with many fathoms of sea water.[9]

One of the main differences that the Mesolithic hunters brought to the Quantocks was to start to open up the forests. Small bald patches, like a case of landscape alopecia, began to appear in the more lightly-wooded areas with the hill ridge starting that path towards the monk-like tonsures so characteristic of the British moorlands today. The Mesolithic is now thought to have seen the start of woodland management for improved hunting yields. Natural openings in the mixed-oak forests attracted herds of grazing animals (and therefore food for their hunters) and so were extended and maintained by ring-barking and summer fires.

WAVE II: FARMING AND SETTLING

At around 4,500 B. C., this part of southern England saw its landscape change again in a profound way. The ability of late stone age people (Neolithic) to grow crops, albeit on a shifting cultivation system, proved critical. With improved food supply, population densities increased and people did not need to be continually on the move. We look here at this second wave in terms of the three agricultural peoples: the Neolithic, the Bronze Age, and the Iron Age.

Phase One: The Neolithic revolution

The Neolithic phase lasted for about two thousand years and was the shortest of the three stone-age periods.[10] While the Palaeolithic legacy was ephemeral and the Mesolithic confined to the hill lands, Neolithic peoples made woodland clearings more widely. Clearance was achieved by either ring-barking and burning of the dead trees or by direct felling using flint axes. This led to patches of land being cleared within the open-hardwood forests to create temporary fields to grow food for cattle. When no longer productive, the clearings were abandoned and then reverted back to forest.

The new settlers migrating into the area continued to use stone tools but brought key new knowledge both of growing crops and of keeping animals. Such knowledge had two important implications. First, groups did not have to be continually on the move; they could establish semi-permanent camps where patches of surrounding land could be cleared for cultivation and a few crops grown. As the land became exhausted so the groups moved on to repeat the process in a new location in a system of shifting cultivation. Although still low, Neolithic population densities were five times that of their Mesolithic forbears. Second, the more secure food supply meant that groups could be larger and could acquire a wider range of material goods: pottery, leather bags, querns for grinding corn. The discovery of Neolithic trackways in the nearby Somerset Levels and the presence of flint tools from distant sites suggest mobility and trade.

Like their predecessors, the Neolithic incomers had to cope with a changing climate and its consequences for flora and fauna. Around 5500 BC the continental climate gradually gave way to a more Atlantic phase with greater rainfall and warmer winters. Pollen records suggest deciduous hardwood species began to dominate with Scots pine falling back and with oak, elm and lime gaining ground. Late in the Neolithic period the climate of southern England again became more continental. This 'Sub-Boreal' phase was marked by warmer, drier summers and colder winters. Along with the climatic changes came ecological shifts with oak and ash dominating the forests scene and hazel also prominent. As Fig. 1.1 shows, the proportion of tree pollen (as a proportion of all pollens in the record) begins to fall in the latter stages of the Neolithic period as trees are progressively felled for farming.

Again, the river gravels at Doniford (Fig. 1.2) have been a rich source for Neolithic finds as for the earlier phases of the stone age. Battlegore (near Williton) is the location of a unique monument from this period, a Neolithic long barrow. Excavated in 1931, it consisted of three stones (one 10ft long and over 2ft thick and another standing in its socket hole) suggesting a burial chamber. An arrowhead and other flint instruments were also found. The stones led to a local legend of a battle between the Devil and the giant of nearby Grabbist Hill, near Dunster. Three later round barrows (of Bronze Age date) and two ring ditches suggest the site remained important over a very long period.

Phase Two: Bronze-age landscapes

Around 2,300 B. C. small groups of newcomers who had been pushing out in a slow-moving invasive wave from south-east Europe eventually arrived in England. They were to be the dominant cultural group for the next millennium and a half. Skeletal evidence suggests they were physically different, slightly shorter and more round-headed, than the Neolithic peoples they gradually displaced.[11] But more critical than any physical differences were the advanced skills and the culture they brought with them. Most important of these skills was a knowledge of working and winning of metals, especially copper and tin, the two metals from which the alloy bronze could be formed. The addition of ten percent of tin to copper produced an alloy which could be cast in moulds and could produce tools with a cutting edge which was superior in performance and endurance to their stone equivalents. Over the centuries bronze manufactures

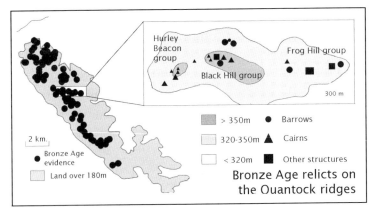

Fig. 3.3 Bronze age structures along the main ridge of the Quantock Hills. (Above) General map of clusters of barrows and cairns. A small section in the central part of the distribution is expanded to show individual structures. (Below) Cairn on Hurley Beacon (1,150 ft) looking west towards Exmoor. Sources: Maps based on Grinsell, 1976, and Riley, 2006 (notes 1 and 2).

became ever more effective and more sophisticated. The higher cost of bronze tools meant that their role may well have been mainly decorative and ceremonial for stone tools continued to be used alongside them.

Although this bronze-making capability led archaeologists to dub the period dominated by these peoples as the 'Bronze Age' this was only one of a series of cultural differences from their Neolithic predecessors. Instead of the long, communal tombs, the newcomers constructed small cairns or round barrows. These were usually the burial places for one (presumably important) person but two or three additional burials were often added later. For Somerset as a whole nearly 800 such round barrows have been recorded, many of them within the Quantock region itself. In her extensive survey of the landscape of the Quantock Hills, Riley records twelve 'clusters' of round barrows. The general location of the groups is shown in Fig.3.3 together with an expanded view of the middle Quantocks around Crowcombe Hill gate.

Many of these hill barrows were excavated in the Victorian period by amateur enthusiasts (often country vicars) looking for grave goods rather than scientific knowledge. You can appreciate the nature of these barrows by walking to any one of the scores on the Quantock ridge. Thorncombe Barrow on the top of Thorncome Hill (1,085 feet) is typical. It is about twenty feet across, about six feet high (and surmounted by an Ordnance Survey triangulation pillar) and surrounded by a shallow ditch. It is a 'bowl barrow' with a shallow depression at its top and has been dug into in many places. No records of archaeological finds have been traced here nor in the several similar barrows which are visible on the surrounding hillside.

But on the lowlands surrounding the hills, evidence is more plentiful. In 1907 a barrow near the present Hinkley Point nuclear stations was excavated by H.St George Gray. It was located at Wick on an outcrop of Lias limestone overlooking Wick Moor which at the time the barrow was constructed was probably an inlet of the sea. It consisted of a small, presumably earlier, barrow over which a structure three times its size had been later constructed as a cairn of limestone blocks. The final barrow was about 75 feet in diameter and ten feet in height. Three burials were found, two entombed with flint implements including a flint dagger and long-necked beakers indicative of the so-called 'Beaker' period. With the excavation backfilled there is today nothing visible but the low mound, but the County Museum at Taunton contains both a model of the barrow and examples of the finds. In view of our discussion of Quantock legend in Chapter 1, we should note in passing that the local Stogursey name for Wick barrow is 'Pixies' Mound' and legends persist of it shifting its position and that if removed by day it will be replaced overnight.

While round barrows in Somerset have not yielded the rich grave goods of some other counties (e.g. gold cups in Cornwall) they do provide valuable clues to Bronze-age life. The presence of jet and metals not found locally point to long-distance trade. Pottery shows major variations in decoration and scale. Flint continued to be used for tools and weapons although bronze and copper implements like the flat axe-head found at Old Cleeve suggests transitions in use. The hoard of bronze weapons and ornaments found near Wick in 1870 contained several copper ingots. Copper was known to be available in the Quantock hills (see Chapter 2 on the geology and Chapter 6 on the Dodington copper mines) but the ingots suggest to some observers that copper was brought in by itinerant traders and processed locally.

Round barrow contents give some clues to the complexity of Bronze Age culture, but many questions remain unanswered: Does the presence of barrow clusters on the upper hills suggest people lived there? Or was burial on the high ground important in prevailing religious beliefs? As on Dartmoor, there is some evidence for Bronze Age hill settlements and field systems at West Hill and Greenaway. Evidence of lowland occupation is likely to have been overridden by many centuries of later agriculture. The record from other counties suggest Bronze Age peoples combined stock rearing and arable farming with hunting. Settlements consisted of circular huts with stone walls and roofs supported by a central upright post. Small fields surrounding the settlements were edged with stone or earthen banks, with barley and sometimes wheat grown. Threshed grain was ground into flour using saddle querns. But as to their population levels or their landscape impact, the enigma remains.

Phase Three: Iron-age landscapes

Towards the end of the Bronze Age, the climate in this part of England began to swing again as the warm, continental climate of the Sub-Boreal phase moved towards the cooler, coastal climate of the Sub-Atlantic phase which – with variations – we continue to have today (Fig. 3.1). Rainfall increased and summer temperatures began to fall. The dominance of oak and ash forests began to give way with more beech and hornbeam and the more northerly species of birch, aspen and juniper. This change coincided from around 700 B. C. when the third great change in the human occupation of the pre-Roman Quantocks began to occur – the Iron Age. We look here at the nature of these peoples and their legacy in the Quantock landscape.[12]

As in the case of Bronze Age peoples, there is no evidence of abrupt invasion but rather a slow process in which groups of newcomers, sometimes small, sometimes large, drifted across southern England as part of a general movement of so-called Celtic peoples in Europe. The process of dispersion and acculturation began in Somerset around 700 B. C. until it was abruptly interrupted (but not eradicated) by the Roman invasion.

The new arrivals differed from the Bronze Age peoples with whom they mingled in two important respects. First, they possessed the knowledge and skills to smelt and work another metal, iron. Iron was much harder than bronze and its fashioning involved both higher smelting temperatures and an understanding of the effects of hammering on metal strength. Iron tools including axes and ploughs were more effective than those possessed by any earlier culture and permitted a greater control over the landscape. As a result, a second major forest clearance phase began. Iron axes were more effective for felling and by the Saxon period, forests were laid waste on a major scale, a change picked up in pollen diagrams by a sharp rise in herb pollens. Trees were replaced by fields, heaths and wood-pastures. Regeneration of forests was prevented by cattle grazing, by cultivation and by heathland fires deliberately lit to get transitory improvement in spring grazing.

A second aspect of iron-age cultures was organizational. They showed an ability to develop more elaborate political structures of tribes headed by chieftains and eventually to meld these into still larger organizations under 'kings'. Along with such organization went a concern for holding territory or 'turfs' and expanding such territories through tribal skirmishing. By the start of the first century BC, three major tribal divisions had developed in Somerset. The Quantocks formed part of the territory of the Dumonnii which extended westwards into Devon and was probably bounded on the east by the Parrett. To the south of Taunton Deane and extending into Dorset were the Durotriges while north Somerset was

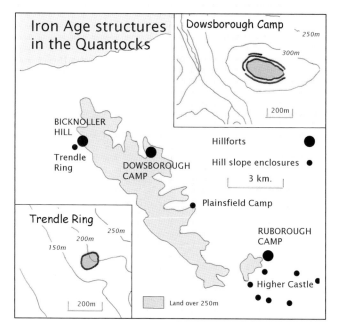

Fig. 3.4 Map of Iron Age structures in the Quantock Hills. The sites of hillforts and hill slope enclosures is shown with enlarged maps of one hillfort (Dowsborough) and one hill-slope enclosure (Trendle Ring) as insets. Source: Riley, 2006 (note 2), 52-53.

occupied by the Dubunni. Given this concern with tribal territory it is not surprising that many of the legacies of the Iron Age peoples today are more concerned with defence and with boundaries than their predecessors.

Fortified hills were characteristic of this period and the Quantocks have several fine examples (Fig.3.4). The most dramatic, which, stands out on the eastern view of the Quantocks is Dowsborough (also called Danesborough or Dawesbury) (Fig.3.5).[13] It consists of a small (six acre) oval enclosure built around the crest of a naturally steep-sided hill. Although now overgrown with scrub oak, it is possible to see its main features. It is surrounded with a single ditch (what the archaeologists call a 'univallate' fort) with entrances on the east and north sides. The round barrow at its western edge is earlier, probably Bronze Age. The view from the fort gives commanding views both across the other Quantock ridges and out across the lowlands to both the sea and the Parrett.

The other two Iron Age forts are also on the eastern flanks of the Quantocks. Plainsfield Camp near Over Stowey is also a univallate fort but only about one third the extent of Dowsborough. Today it is surrounded by forestry plantations and the ramparts are somewhat overgrown. Ruborough Camp ('ruborough' meaning 'rough hill') in the southern Quantocks is a triangular-shaped promontory fort. The site is unusual in having two lines of defence with the inner ramparts surrounding an area of four acres, smaller than that of Dowsborough. There are three causeways across the outer works but these may be due to later farm use. Ruborough is one of a group of three small forts in the southern Quantocks with Higher Castles and Rook's Castle (see Fig. 3.4).

Fig. 3.5 Traces of Iron-Age activity in the Quantock Hills. The reinforced vallum around Dowsborough Camp viewed across Hodders Combe sharpens the natural outline of the hill.

In addition to the these three structures there are others whose purpose is less clear. Trendle Ring above Bicknoller village can be clearly seen from the A358. It is a ring-shaped structure on a steeply-sloping hillside, about a third the area of Dowsborough Camp, and surrounded by a bank and ditch. Other partly-formed forts are located at Elworthy Barrows on the Brendons and in Broomfield parish. The purpose of these 'hill forts' has been hotly debated. Clearly they involved a considerable investment to build them and this points to strong tribal organization to bring the resources together. But did they contain permanent or seasonal settlements or were they for ceremonial use?

A second type of Iron Age structure is illustrated by Dead Woman's Ditch (Plate 7B) on the Quantock Hills above Over Stowey. It consists of a linear rampart up to six feet in height and with a ditch on the western side. It runs from Robin Uprights Hill downslope towards the Ramscombe valley and was probably a boundary marker of some kind. It can be easily found today from the car park which bears its name. The association of the site name with the notorious murder of Jenny Walford by the charcoal burner, John Walford in July 1789 is tempting but map evidence spoils the link by showing that the name predates the crime.

For evidence on the type of settlements and way of life of Iron Age peoples we need to travel a few miles east of the Quantocks to the Somerset levels. Meare lake village near Glastonbury provides examples of complex lake-side dwellings with a heavy dependence on fishing and wildfowling. The seven centuries of Iron Age occupation went through several phases of increasing sophistication with prehistorians identifying distinctive phases such as 'Hallstat' and 'La Tene' based on type-studies at German and French sites respectively. The period was to come to an end not with the slow mixing of previous cultural transitions but with the abrupt overprinting of an external force– the Roman invasion.

WAVE III: IMPERIAL OCCUPATION [3.3]

Unlike the earlier 'invasions' which were slow and diffuse, the Roman occupation of Somerset was swift and sharply defined.[14] The Roman conquest began in A.D. 43 and was to last for four hundred years. It began with the second Augusta legion under Vespasian fighting their way westwards across Somerset as part of the invasion of the southwest with strong resistance being met around the two Iron Age fortresses of Ham Hill and South Cadbury. Military occupation was accompanied by strategic road building with the line along the Polden Hills from the Fosse Way at Ilchester being a critical portal for west Somerset. Roman rule brought the Quantock country for the first time an imperial rule that ran from the Scottish borders in the north across the Mediterranean to Galilee in the east.

The 'Pax Romana'

Although Somerset can boast such fine examples of Roman occupation as the settlements at Bath and Ilchester or the 'Dido and Aeneas' pavement from Low Ham, the imprint on the Quantock country has proved harder to find. A hundred years ago, archaeologists regarded the lands west of the Parrett and north of the Tone as fringe territory of little interest to the Romans compared to the mineral working of Mendip or the urban glories of Aquae Sulis. But as the results of decades of patient excavation has accumulated, so a fuller picture of the Roman imprint in the western marchlands is starting to emerge. A summary of the evidence available to date is shown in the map (Fig. 3.6).

Field evidence of Roman occupation in the Quantocks is of several kinds. Roman coins were the most striking but most capricious. A scatter of random finds around Watchet was supplemented by two major hoards at Stringston and

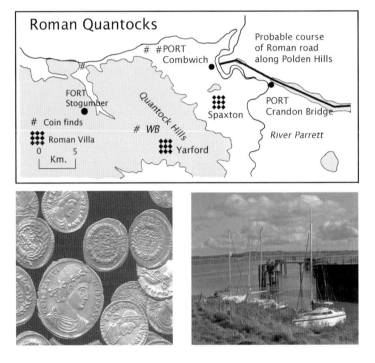

Fig. 3.6 The Quantocks in the Roman period. (Above) Evidence for forts, villas, roads and ports in the region. The lower course of the River Parrett is speculative as is the precise line of the Roman road along the crest of the Polden Hills. WB = West Bagborough. (Below left) Roman silver coins of the fourth-century found by a metal 'detectorist' in 2001 in a hoard in an arable field at West Bagborough. (Below right) This small and unprepossessing inlet on the tidal Parrett, Combwich Pill, was in use in Roman times. It lay, via a ferry across the river from the Pawlett Hams, at the western end of the Roman road along the Poldens linking to major settlements at Bath and Ilchester. Sources: Photo of coins courtesy of Somerset Museum Service.

West Bagborough. The latter was found by metal detectors in 2001. It consists of 680 silver coins mostly from the fourth century, minted in the reigns of the emperors Constantius II and Julian and struck in places as distant as Arles (in southern France), Triers (in Germany), and Rome itself. There were also over seventy pieces of blank silver, possibly intended for pieces of jewellery. The hoard, which can be viewed in Taunton museum, suggests something of the richness that Rome brought to the Quantock foothills.

Excavations at both Combwich and at Crandon Bridge suggest both locations were used as ports on the left and right banks of the lower Parrett, linked to the Polden highway from Ilchester. Air photographs show evidence of other Roman legacies: rectangular field enclosures at Bishops Lydeard, a settlement near Hinkley Point, and a fort near Stogumber are typical. Evidence for villas, the diagnostic unit of Roman agriculture, are also now firmly established for the Quantocks. The first discovered by a farmer in 1962 lies between Enmore and Charlynch close to the Durleigh Brook. Excavations showed the wall footings of a range of buildings, pottery (from the third and fourth centuries) and an elaborate mosaic with a floral motif. The second lies four miles to the southwest above the hamlet of Yarford. It was excavated in 2007 and found to be a small 'portico' type of villa with main and secondary blocks of rooms, a bath house, and a fine mosaic with a theme associated with Bacchus, the god of wine. Both villas show that Roman cultivation had pushed much further west in the county than previously expected.

The accumulation of such evidence now suggests that the Quantocks were firmly within the Roman pale. Not endowed with the mineral riches of the Mendips or the agricultural fecundity of south and east Somerset but with the *pax Romana* allowing the steady build up of settlement and population to levels not to be seen again until the peak of the Medieval period.

Roman withdrawal and the 'dark ages'

Withdrawal of Roman forces early in the fifth century marked the end of that stability and the beginning of a darker and more turbulent age.[15] By 410 Rome had severed its connections with its former colony and Quantock Somerset was left to fend for itself. Evidence from Yarford suggests damage was done to the existing villa and many strands of economic life must have unravelled. It would be another three centuries before Anglo-Saxon rule brought a new and different order.

These centuries following the withdrawal of Roman forces are ones where documentation is poor. But whether the label 'Dark Ages' for this 300-year long period is justified or not remains a source of controversy. Maritime contacts with both Wales to the north and Ireland to the west became more important. In west Somerset, Christianity was introduced in the fifth and sixth centuries by British

Fig. 3.7 A number of coastal churches in south-west England were established by Celtic mission-aries from Ireland and Wales. St Decuman is commemorated in this modern pebble mosaic in Watchet. Decuman was reputed to have landed in the sixth century and his name lives on in the dedication of the parish church of Watchet.

missionaries arriving from Wales and we see that legacy today in the names of parish churches. St Dubricius at Porlock, recalling the Welsh bishop St Dyfrig (died c550), is one of a series along the coast recording the names of Celtic saints. In the Quantocks, the key example is at Watchet, with the dedication of the parish church to St Decuman. Legends surround this sixth-century Celtic saint, including his arrival as a holy man voyaging across the Severn Estuary on an insubstantial coracle with his cow (Fig. 3.7). He was later martyred by the Watchet folk but reputed to have washed off his severed head in a nearby well. Today the Holy Well survives a few yards from his church.

Whatever the legends, the early missionary work meant that the Saxon peoples who later moved into the area were colonizing an area where Christianity already had a hold. Excavations from 1962 near Cannington Hill (Cynwit castle) of a large Romano-British cemetery have added to the evidence: many of the 5,000 graves are aligned in what was to become a Christian rather than pagan fashion.

WAVE IV: SAXON SETTLEMENT [3.4]

The Saxon colonists were Germanic peoples from different parts of north-west Europe and, although they were thought to share a common culture and basic language, they were not a unified group. Exactly when the Saxon peoples arrived in Somerset is not known; they may well have colonized the area as small groups over several centuries rather than as a single wave. Certainly from 700 they were the dominant group and their farms and hamlets were well established in the Quantock area. Here we look at the legacy of the Saxon peoples in terms of their villages and towns, their place-names and their organization, all of which we inherit today.

The legacy of settlements

For the best evidence of the extent of 'Saxon' settlement in the Quantocks we have to turn to a document written twenty years after the Saxon hegemony had been succeeded by the Norman. A fuller analysis of Domesday book is given at the start of the next chapter but it is logical to treat here the pattern of settlement it shows at the Saxon 'high watermark'.[16] Saxon places were widely established over the lowlands surrounding the Quantocks (Fig. 3.8) but there were few habitations above 650 feet. A ring of settlements looped around the Quantock Hills like a necklace, mostly located on the break of slope. Here water-supply from streams was plentiful, land quality downslope from the village was good for tillage, while upslope was land for grazing, felling, and peat digging.[17] Only a few settlements such as Aisholt and Broomfield were at higher elevations but these too were located in combes rather than on the ridges. Away from the hills settlement was more complex with a few large villages but many small hamlets. For reasons of ecclesiastical land ownership (see discussion in the next chapter) the part of the region which extends onto the Vale of Taunton Deane recorded fewer places in the Domesday survey and probably underestimates Saxon settlement.

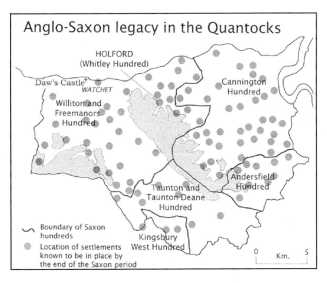

Fig. 3.8 Anglo-Saxon legacy in the Quantocks. The map shows the location of settlements that were known to be in existence in the eleventh century at the end of the Saxon period. The boundaries of the Saxon land division, the hundred, is also shown.

But not all Saxon settlements were rural in character. The Saxon king, Edward, planned a defensive system for the Wessex coastline in the early tenth century based on the concept of 'burghs' and Watchet was selected to be one of these.[18] A burgh was a major settlement with a coastal harbour or bridging point on a river where an earth bank and ditch could be built to protect its population against a Danish attack from the sea. By Edward's time the Danes had occupied the islands of Steep Holm and Flat Holm and were using these as bases for raids on vulnerable Saxon settlements along the coast of the Bristol Channel. Watchet's defences were located west of the present port and may have been built by King Alfred. They appear to have staved off a Danish attack in 914 but the raiders were successful in 988 when 'Watchet was ravaged, Goda was killed and many died with him' and again in 996 when 'great evil and in burning and manslaying was wrought there.' The remnants of the earthworks can be seen today at 'Daws Castle' (the name commemorating Thomas Dawe, a sixteenth-century landowner) at the top of some rapidly eroding Blue Lias cliffs. The original defensive works of a low wall and wide bank were strengthened after the Danish raids by a second wider wall and deeper ditch. Because of cliff erosion the full extent of the structure is difficult to judge but the remaining area covers about five acres.

The relationship between the fortified structure and the port settlement of Watchet remains obscure but the latter must also have had some defences. Its importance as a Saxon burgh was strengthened in 980 when it became one of several (up to ten) mints operating in Somerset. Coins were struck from then until 1056, the mint resuming in 1080 after Norman occupation. Examples of the coins and the subsequent story of the town can be seen in the fascinating museum by the harbour. Watchet remains today as it probably was in Saxon times, the most populous place in the Quantock country.

The place name legacy

Saxon charters detailing the extent of land holdings and their boundaries are extant from 700 onwards.[19] Inevitably, such charters needed to refer to recognizable landmarks, be they natural or man-made features. The most obvious natural feature were the Quantock Hills themselves and, as we noted in our opening chapter, the word for the Quantocks is first mentioned in a Saxon document.[20] Hill names occur in a number of places. Charlynch is 'Ceolred's hill', Kilton is 'Cylfantum' in the will of King Alfred (he left it to his son and successor, Edward the Elder) and possibly means the 'settlement by the hill'. Both Bishops Lydeard ('Lidigeard' in 854) and Lydeard St Lawrence include the Celtic 'garth' = ridge, but the first syllable is unclear 'led' = grey is possible, rendering Lydeard as 'grey hill'.

The steep-sided valleys around the Quantocks, the combes, are also first recorded in Saxon documents as in village names as at Combe Florey.

Hestercombe, first mentioned in an 854 document as 'Hegsteldescumb' probably means 'bachelors valley' or 'warriors valley while Crowcombe is self-evidently 'valley of the crows'. Further west Nettlecombe is 'the valley where the nettles grow'. Other streams which drained the valleys also gave rise to distinctive names which remain today. Bilbrook near Old Cleeve is the 'stream where the watercress grows', and Monksilver (originally called Silver ['Sulffiere' in 897], Monachorum was added in the 1113) the silvery stream. Williton ('Willetun' in 904) is 'the settlement on the Willett[stream]' and Holford is 'the ford in the hollow'. Coastal features are recorded in the remote hamlet of Steart from the Saxon 'steort' meaning promontory.

Some place names give a clue to the local vegetation. Aisholt, the most remote of the Quantock parishes, recalls 'the ash copse'. Bicknoller ('Bykenalre') is 'Bica's alder tree' and Durleigh 'wood frequented by deer'. Watchet whose name occurs as 'Waeced' in 917 and 'Wecedport' in 987 may be the Celtic for 'below the wood'.

Other Quantock places simply have the owners name, often added to the term 'ton' (= settlement) and 'stock' (= farm, possibly dairy farm). Thus Fiddington is the 'settlement of Fita's people', Cothelstone is 'Cuthwulfs settlement', and Lilstock the 'farm of Fita's people'. Sometimes the personal name was added later so Stogumber was originally known as 'Stoke' and 'Gomer' added in 1225. Sampford Brett was originally known as 'Sampford' (the 'sandy ford') and Brett only added in Norman times to indicate its Breton owner. Today's maps and signposts continue to show how far the naming of the land was dominantly a Saxon legacy.

The organizational legacy

Another subtle legacy of the Saxon occupation which has persisted, albeit in revised form, right up to the present is the system of land division. At the most local level, some of the land boundaries on the Quantocks date back to Saxon times and even some of the stone markers may be very ancient (see Fig. 3.9 and Plate 7C). But such divisions go much higher. The Quantocks form part of the county of Somerset, one of the Saxon shires into which the kingdom of Wessex was divided shortly after occupation.[21] The name Somerset probably meant 'the land of the summer pastures', a reference to the fine grazing land lying north of the county capital (Somerton) in the Somerset levels. The shire was a unit for collecting taxes and administering justice with the 'Shire-reeve' or sheriff its most important legal officer.

Each shire was divided into parts called 'hundreds' (see Fig. 3.8). Like the shires they had administrative, judicial and military functions, some of which they retained into the modern period. Their name probably stems from the fact that they originally consisted of 100 'hides', a hide being a unit of land taxation.

Fig. 3.9   Stone markers are a feature of western moorland landscapes such as Dartmoor and Exmoor and may mark Iron Age or Saxon territories. The dates of these two Quantock stones are unknown and both have been restored in recent times. Triscombe Stone (left) and the smaller Longstone (right) on Longstone Hill.

Estimates of the value of a hide vary but it seems to have referred to the land unit needed to maintain an extended peasant family, estimated at values from 40 up to 120 acres depending on the productivity of the land being farmed. By the late eleventh century we know the Quantock region was part of four hundreds: Andersfield [9] and Cannington [34] to the east of the Quantock Hills, Taunton and Taunton Deane [25] to the south, and Williton and Freemanors [57] to the west. The numbers in square brackets refer to the total number of settlements recorded in each hundred in 1086. Today the three district councils which jointly share administration of the Quantock region reflect the Saxon hundred divisions laid down more than a millennium ago. Thus Sedgemoor District, administered from Bridgwater incorporates the Andersfield and Cannington hundreds.

Below the level of the hundred lay the basic building block of the parish (see Fig. 1.13). As Norman Pounds has argued, the parish formed a constant in the territorial structure of administration both secular and religious from its first introduction in the fourth century until the first half of the nineteenth.[22] The Saxon period saw its rapid diffusion, first through the larger *parochia* of the minster church and later the smaller 'parish' of the late Saxon period. We shall rely heavily on parish records for the rest of this book.

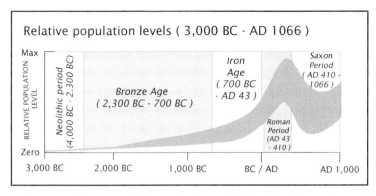

Fig. 3.10 Relative population trends for England over the last four thousand years. The shaded band gives the likely range of values. Source: Simmons, 2001 (note 23), 67.

Population

The long duration covered in this chapter extended back over more than seventy millennia and closed in the middle eleventh century only one millennium short of the present. One way of summarizing the period is to look at estimates of resident population. For England as a whole, populations for the latter half of that period are shown in Fig. 3.10 based on the work of archaeologist Peter Fowler.[23] Some parts of the curve, such as the acceleration of growth in the Iron Age and the decline after the Roman withdrawal are well established. The broad band on the graph shows we are dealing with probabilities only, not precise estimates.

England's total population at the height of the Roman occupation was probably approaching four million. It fell dramatically after Roman withdrawal but had built up again by the end of the Saxon period. How big the population of Quantock country was at any stage before the Domesday survey can be no more than informed guesswork. Until the start of land cultivation (shifting rather than sustained cultivation) in the Neolithic, any population was largely transient perhaps visiting the area in hunting or foraging bands in the summer and autumn months. If we assume that our area sustained population densities that were roughly on a par with the England-wide average (itself a heroic assumption for they may well have been lower), then the Quantocks were an almost empty landscape until the Neolithic. On a pro-rata density basis, the Quantock population would have reached 100 by the Iron Age, peaked at 3,000 in the Roman period, dropped to 1,000 in the Dark Ages and grown again to over 4,000 by the Norman Conquest.

From a soaring glider, the view of Quantock country 12,000 years ago would have looked like southern Greenland today. By 9,000 the scene would have changed via Canadian tundra to an almost unbroken hardwood forest. By 6,000 years ago small gaps might have appeared as the late Mesolithic peoples manipulated the woodland to improve hunting. Over the next five millennia widening gaps in that forest would have shown the hand of human settlers so that by the Norman conquest the broad shape of Quantock settlement would be in place. In the next four chapters we turn to that critical last millennium and trace the huge changes wrought there.

Four

MEDIEVAL MODIFICATIONS

And there the God-place sits
While the seasons circle
Within the circling years.
There is birth and death
But all are gathered to the smiling hills
To be mothered and breasted
In warm red earth.

Revd. Arthur Moss, *Aisholt and its Church* (1995)[1]

Arthur Moss had the privilege of being priest in charge of this Quantock 'God-place' (All Saints parish church, Aisholt: see Plate 8A) during his long period as vicar of neighbouring Cannington from 1958 to 1980. The stanza is taken from his poem about his church, written to accompany a small guide. He loved the church ('squatting on the edge of its vast green space') and so do I. It is the most remote, though not the highest, of the Quantock benefices. Like the tiny settlement it served, it was founded in the Saxon period probably by a hermit priest who made himself a dwelling and oratory, sited near the stream but just above the floodwater's reach. In location and in form and plan it reminds me of early Cornish churches. There may be Norman elements in one of the windows (formerly a door) on the pulpit side but the chancel is medieval, probably built around 1340 and rebuilt in the fifteenth century. In his diary, Coleridge writes of Aisholt as that 'green, romantic chasm' and he tried (without success) in 1800 to persuade his wife Sarah to move from Nether Stowey and take a house there to be near to his friends in the vicarage.[2]

But what gives Aisholt special significance for understanding the medieval Quantocks is that it marks a high watermark, where the tide of settlement had washed into every corner of that region. The medieval period (latin *medius* = middle) can be defined in several ways. Here we follow convention and mark its limits by two great events in English history: the Norman Conquest of 1066 and the dissolution of the monasteries by Henry VIII in the middle of the sixteenth century. Over the intervening 500 years much of the Quantock landscape was stamped out and we can see that medieval legacy all around us today.

The organization of the chapter divides into four parts. First, we look at the Norman legacy, both the great record of human occupation, (the Domesday survey of 1086) and the impact of Norman organization on the landscape. Second, we recognize the critical impact of the medieval church on the Quantocks especially in the middle and later phases of the medieval age. Third, we consider the economic life of the medieval Quantocks both through the expansion of agriculture on the one hand and trade and industry on the other. Finally, we look at the rather scanty evidence for population change and the implied impact of the Black Death on the area.

THE NORMAN LEGACY

Although 'Norman' in the legal sense refers to the reign of just four monarchs and spans only nine decades, it saw the start of a profound change in English (and with it, Quantock) society and landscape. Although the royal succession after 1156 was to switch from one French province (Normandy, the seat of the Norman dukes) to another (Anjou, the seat of the Plantagenets) the language, the system of government, and control of England became dominantly French rather than Anglo-Saxon over the next two centuries. Even within two decades of the Norman conquest, all but five percent of English land came under the control of French rather than English landlords. We look first at the record of the Domesday Book then the physical legacy of the Norman years in the built landscape.

Quantock places in the Domesday survey

Domesday Book gives an intricate picture of the England of 1086.[3] It was prepared by order of William the Conqueror as a massive survey to ensure that all landowners and their tenants should be recorded for the assessment and collection of the 'geld' or land tax. The information was collected by commissioners through local juries giving evidence on oath. It includes details of the property of all landowners, their lands, manors and men, whether they were freemen or slaves, farmers or cottagers; their ploughteams, horses and other stock, as well as the services and rents paid to or by them; the names of the previous landowners in the time of King Edward the Confessor (TRE = *Tempore Regis Edwardi*) and the value of their lands then (TRE) and in 1086..

Crowcombe on the western side of the Quantocks provides a typical Domesday entry. It reads:

Robert the Constable holds CROWCOMBE from the Count [of Mortain]. St Swithin's Church, Winchester, held it before 1066. 10 hides. But they did not pay tax except for 4 hides. Land for 12 ploughs, of which 1 hide is in lordship; 3 ploughs there; 6 slaves; 31 villagers; and 10 small-holders with 10 ploughs and 9 hides. Meadow, 11 acres; woodland, 20 acres; pasture 1 league long and ½ league wide. 26 cattle; 26 pigs; 70 sheep; 28 goats; The value was and is £8.[4]

The original entries are in Latin, often in a highly abbreviated almost 'short-hand' form. Place-names cannot always be securely identified and some terms in the accounts are obscure. For example 'hide' is a measure of taxable land but, although nominally 120 acres, it varies in size considerably from place to place depending on such factors as land quality and type of agriculture.

The text of the Domesday book is listed under landholders, beginning with royal properties, followed by ecclesiastical and then lay landowners. For example King William and Queen Edith held 35 properties throughout Somerset, including seven in the Quantocks: notably Cannington and Williton (see Fig. 4.1). But the largest landowner in our region was Roger of Courselles (Courselles is near Falaise in Normandy) a major Somerset landowner who held one third of all the Quantock places. The second most important landowner was William of Mohun (another Norman lord) who held extensive lands in west

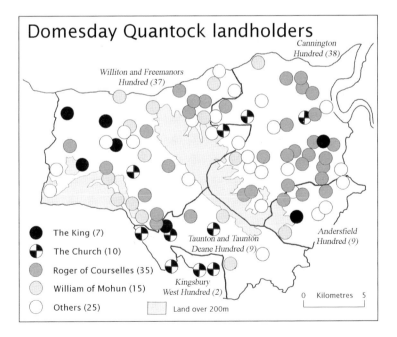

Fig. 4.1 Land ownership in the eleventh century. Major holders of estates at the time of the Domesday survey are shown Map based on data in the Domesday survey of 1086 (see sources in note 3).

Somerset around his castle base at Dunster and who held fourteen Quantock places mainly in the west of the region. Altogether, the 92 Domesday places listed are scattered between twenty owners, some owning a single manor as in the case of William of Falaise who owned one of the most important, Stogursey.

The total number of separate places mentioned in Domesday records for Somerset are 612; of these 92 fell within the Quantock region. A third refer to settlements which survive today as familiar villages and parishes (see parish map in Fig. 1.13); the rest are hamlets and farms. But not all modern villages are mentioned in Domesday book. Of the two unrecorded in this area, Cothelstone was probably a tacit inclusion in what the historian F. W. Maitland has called the 'colossal manor of Taunton Deane'.[5] Dodington is also missing though its name suggests a Saxon foundation: it may well have been hidden within the manor of Nether Stowey. A single parish may contain several entries: thus Spaxton contains entries not only for Spaxton itself but for six outlying settlements (at Currypool, Pightley, Merridge, Radlet, Swang, and Tuxwell). Such dispersion in outlying hamlets and farms seems more prevalent in this area of west Somerset than in the east of the county where agglomeration into large compact villages was more common.

Identification of some Domesday places is tricky. Two or more places may bear the same name (e.g. Nether and Over Stowey) and it is not clear whether one or more separate units existed in the eleventh century. In others (e.g. Lexworthy hamlet) two or three entries may refer to the same place. In still other cases groups of places are described together in combined entries; thus the returns for the royal manors of Cannington and Williton are amalgamated with a third manor (Carhampton) lying west of our region.

Wealth, population and land

As we saw for the entry for Crowcombe, Domesday gives several measures of the prosperity of a place: (1) assessment stated in terms of hides (often subdivided into virgates and ferlings); (2) plough lands; (3) plough teams; (4) population subdivided into five categories (villeins, bordars, serfs, cottars and coliberts; and (5) values both for 1086 and some earlier year. No great changes in wealth accompanied the first twenty years of Norman occupation. Of the eighty Quantock places that have comparable data for 1086 and when the land was acquired (TRE) from its Saxon owners, the majority had unchanged values. In the thirty that changed, those increasing outnumbered those falling in value by 2:1. A majority of those with 'rising' values were located in the foothills of the Brendons, possibly due to active colonization west of Stogumber.

An 'average' Quantock settlement at this time would have had just a dozen recorded people (six villagers, four smallholders and one slave). Assuming that the people who were counted had family members (say, a wife and children) then,

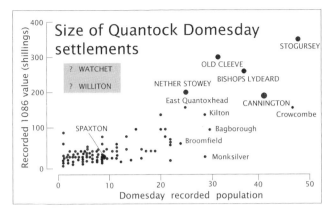

Fig. 4.2 Size of Quantock Domesday settlements, 1086. The graph plots the recorded population number on the horizontal axis against value in shillings on the vertical axis. The eight largest Quantock settlements today (2010) are shown in capitals: data not available for Watchet and Williton.

when grossed up this might be equivalent to a small hamlet of forty or so people: the multiplier used by demographers is commonly x3.5. But averages tend to skew the picture. Detailed examination shows a clear hierarchy of settlements with today's leading settlements (Cannington, Stogursey and Nether Stowey to the east of the Quantocks and Crowcombe, Bagborough, Bishops Lydeard to the west) standing out above the rest (Fig. 4.2). Also important were a group of coastal villages from West Quantoxhead through to Kilton and Lilstock all with the equivalent of a hundred inhabitants (using our rough multiplier). If these 'super' villages are allowed for, then the typical unit of settlement over most of the rest of the region falls as low as eight recorded inhabitants. A quarter of all settlements had four or fewer people and were the equivalent of isolated farms only.

Flying over the Quantocks a thousand years ago we would be most likely to see below a dominantly wooded area with cultivated fields near each Domesday settlement and grazing land further away. Beyond lay the woodland. In the Domesday record, extent of woodland in any place was indicated in two ways as shown in Fig. 4.3.[6] The more usual method was to record the acreage of wood (ranging from 6 to 129 acres in the Quantocks). But in some cases dimensions of the wood are given in leagues and furlongs. At Newhall the ambiguous measurement of 'half a league of wood' is recorded, while at Quantock eight acres of underwood (*silvae minutae*) merit special mention. The pattern shown indicates the heavily wooded character of both the Ilfracombe Beds of the southern Quantocks (an area of royal forest) and of the Liassic clays of the coastal Kilve – Holford area. Relative to the rest of South-West England the Quantocks stand out as heavily wooded.

Entries for meadow land are uniformly given in acres. Meadow was the best grassland whose main purpose was to produce a hay crop each year and thus

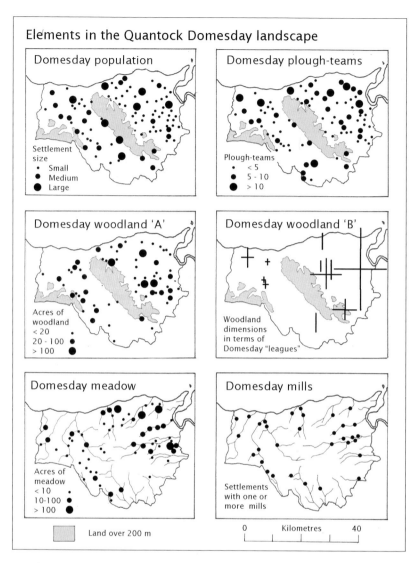

Fig. 4.3 Elements in the Quantock landscape in the Domesday survey of 1086. Population, plough-teams, two measures of woodland, meadow and mills are shown. Source: Redrawn from Finn & Wheatley, 1967 (note 5).

provide the winter feed for the plough oxen. All animals had to be off the meadow by Ladyday. Whatever the exact size of the Domesday acre, the total meadow amount was understandably much less than that of woodland. Entries of more than 30 acres of meadow are rare, half the manors had less than five acres, and on the upland manors none is recorded.

Meadowland probably lay in the valley bottoms and was carefully distinguished from the widespread pasture of the poorer upland areas. Villages with abundant pasture tend to be found bordering those hill areas unsuitable for tillage. Marsh is noted only rarely with Fiddington (43 acres) and Tuxwell (41 acres) on the eastern slopes the only Quantock entries. Livestock is recorded on the demesne (the lord's land) and not for the settlement as a whole. Of the animals recorded sheep are dominant making up two-thirds of the total. Pigs and goats, in roughly equal numbers, make up a further sixth

Records of built structures in Domesday concentrate on mills. These occur in two out of five Somerset Domesday entries; in the Quantock region this rises to over half. There were four mills on the three Lexworthy entries and this, together with the reference to paying six 'blooms' (= ingots of iron), may imply the use of water mills to power forges.[7] As Fig. 4.3 shows, mills were widely distributed throughout the region especially around the foot of the Quantock Hills where swift-flowing streams emerged from the combes.

Churches are rarely mentioned in Domesday and only Cannington and Stogumber figure in the Quantock accounts. Equally, information about urban life is sparse. The entry for Watchet is puzzling: it had been a Saxon burgh with a mint in pre-Conquest time (see Chapter 3). But in 1086 it is recorded as only a small manor with half a plough team for its single plough-land, with two recorded inhabitants and a mill.

Norman castles, towns and churches

Since Domesday gives a useful but often ambiguous account of the Norman presence in the Quantocks, we need to look in the landscape for other evidence. For the north-east Quantocks, Fig. 4.4 plots examples of Norman building of castle, town and church during that period.[8]

Castles were an essential element in extending the network of Norman power and control over newly-occupied country. Domesday itself makes reference to only two castles in Somerset, Dunster (the stronghold of the de Mohuns) west of the region and Montacute (Count of Mortain, half brother of William the Conqueror) to the south. But within a century, three castles can be traced in our region. The earliest was at Over Stowey and Robert Dunning suggests that this may have been in existence in late Saxon times as a focus for the Quantock royal forest for King Harold (killed at the battle of Hastings) and simply taken over by the Normans. Today all that remains is a jumble of earthmarks and a low mound at Castle Field near Parsonage Farm to the north of the present village. In contrast, the remains of a second castle at Nether Stowey (possibly built to replace the one at Over Stowey) are clear today (Fig. 4.4). It was built by William Fitzodo before 1150. Constructed on a small hill overlooking the village on a classic motte-and-bailey Norman pattern, it subsequently passed to the Audley family before being abandoned by 1485. The grassed-over foundations of the rectangular stone keep (60 x 50 feet) are clearly visible today as are the double moat and bailey earthworks that surround and defend it.

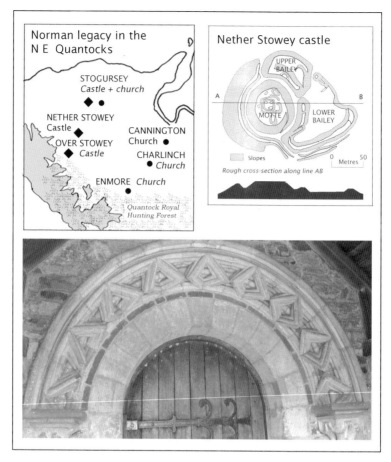

Fig. 4.4 Norman elements in the landscape of the NE Quantock foothills. (Upper left) Map of castles and churches. (Upper right) Plan and cross-section of the earthworks of Nether Stowey castle. (Below) Norman doorway in the parish church of Enmore. Sources: Dunning, 1995, and Riley, 2006 (note 8).

Two miles north near the village of Stogursey lies a third castle. It is first mentioned in 1090 and may have been built by the de Courcy family. This was the largest and most complex of the three, with stone curtain wall, towers and an inner and outer bailey. Only parts of the stone walls, the moat, and a small house built into the original gate house are visible today. It was held for King John in 1215 but subsequent orders to destroy it seem to have been ignored. It was finally burnt down in 1457 during the Wars of the Roses; it has remained a ruin since.

Stogursey is important, not just for its castle, but as an example of a Norman new town.[9] Granted to William de Falaise whose father had fought at Hastings, the manor of Stogursey passed on his death to his daughter Emma. On her marriage to a William de Curci (steward of Henry I), the place became known as Stoke Curci (modified by Somerset drawl over the years to Stogursey). The

Curcis had founded a borough here by 1225 with rights to weekly markets and two fairs during the year; at one stage it sent two members to Parliament. Four lanes converge on Stogursey from the surrounding countryside of scattered farms, meeting in the wide street that was the central market place. As in so many English towns part of the original market place has been infilled, at Stogursey by a row of cottages on the south side. Such houses form a continuous façade giving it an urban, even a French, feel and behind the street line the narrow, rectangular plots of the town burgesses (the burgage tenements) stretch back as narrow gardens.

Stogursey's failure to thrive as a Norman town lies in many causes. Unlike Bridgwater it was not a trading port and Combwich was its nearest river access. During the wars of the thirteenth century, the fact that Stogursey Priory belonged to a French abbey (Lonlay) meant that its revenues were seized by the Crown. Finally, in 1414 the priory was confiscated with Eton College and Kings College, Cambridge, as the beneficiaries.

Today, the finest evidence of a Norman presence in Stogursey lies in its parish church, regarded by Berta Lawrence, as the 'cathedral of the Quantocks'.[10] It was built as the priory church of St Andrew at Stogursey around 1090 by William de Falaise. It has Norman round arches supporting the crossing tower and the north and south transepts (Fig. 4.5). A century later the chancel was extended to form a choir and the circular apses removed. The decorations on the Norman arches show typical zig-zag and dog's tooth designs.

Fig. 4.5 The finest example of Norman architecture in the Quantock region is the Priory Church of St Andrew, Stogursey. The characteristic Romanesque style of the rounded crossing and transept arches and (inset) examples of the intricately carved pier capitals.

The only other church in the region to show major Norman features is St Michael's at Enmore. This was built by another Norman family, the Malets, around 1185 and the south doorway shows the same rounded form and elaborate zigzag and dog-tooth design (Fig. 4.4). We may guess that many other Norman-style churches were built across the Quantocks but these were so extensively rebuilt during the explosion of church rebuilding in the later medieval phases that little evidence remains. Occasionally, as where herringbone masonry survives in the north wall of the nave of St Andrews at Old Cleeve, fragments of the work of Norman masons can be traced.

THE MEDIEVAL CHURCH IN THE LANDSCAPE

One of the glorious medieval legacies of the Quantock parishes is the richness of its parish churches. As local historian Joe Bettey puts it:[11]

> Few counties can rival Somerset in the number, splendour and interest of its medieval churches. They remain a remarkable tribute to the enduring appeal of the Christian message for Somerset people, and make clear to even the casual observer that the Middle Ages were above all an age of faith.

We look here at how the pattern of parish churches evolved, both geographically across the area and within a single church building. We then turn to the second arm of the Quantock church: abbeys and priories. Their distribution is shown in Fig. 4.6. For those interested in visiting individual churches, the

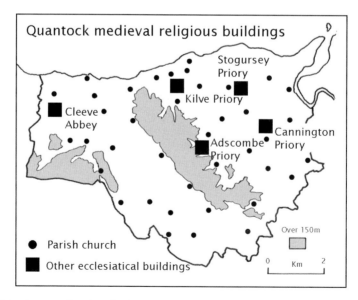

Fig. 4.6 Distribution of medieval religious buildings in the Quantocks. Parish churches, abbeys and priories are shown.

Pevsner volume remains indispensable as do the excellent pamphlets available in many buildings.[12]

The Quantock parish church

By the start of the medieval period, the pattern of Somerset parishes, each with its own church, was effectively complete. In 909 the county had been split off from the original Wessex-wide diocese based at Winchester, to become a diocese in its own right with its own bishop based at a cathedral church at Wells. 'Planting' of individual churches was frequently hierarchic with a set of central or 'minster' churches (each with a group of resident clergy) who served both it and a set of satellite, smaller 'daughter' churches around it. The Quantocks had their own late-Saxon minster churches, Stogumber to the west and Nether Stowey and Spaxton to the east.

The process of church colonization outwards from these minsters is illustrated by the small parish of Elworthy set on the eastern slopes of the Brendon Hills (see Fig. 8.8). Originally part of Stogumber, the foundation of the present small church dedicated to St Martin of Tours probably goes back to these times. But the first written record was much later (1233) when William Malet gave it to the Order of St John of Jerusalem and rectors were appointed to that order until 1540. Now redundant, the western tower and two tiny lancet windows (one in the west wall of the tower, one in the north-west corner of the nave) survive from that period.

In visiting such churches it is important to separate out the foundation date from the architecture you now see. Most church foundations were late Saxon but likely to have been very small structures, constructed of local wood and thus having constantly to be repaired and rebuilt. Only when stone is used may the record survive with evidence likely to be found in ground-level foundations or in stone re-used in later building. This process of elaboration and extension over the centuries is nowhere better seen than in the parish church at Nettlecombe. This church is located hard by Nettlecombe Court (Plate 11A), the twin symbols of temporal and spiritual authority in this western parish on the edge of the Brendons.[13] There is no mention of a church here in the Domesday record and it seems likely that Nettlecombe was a daughter chapel of the Stogumber minster church and a wooden-built structure. The stages by which the church has grown over the medieval period is shown in Fig. 4.7. In (A) the church consisted of a simple, box-like structure built from local stone around 1250. It was aligned east-west with the smaller chancel (with its altar) to the east and the larger nave (for the congregation) to the west. By 1453 (B) three elements had been added. First a church porch on the north side of the nave. Its location is unusual (most parish churches have their entrance porch on the south side) and reflects the position of the church close by the lord's house. Second, a rood screen, separating nave and

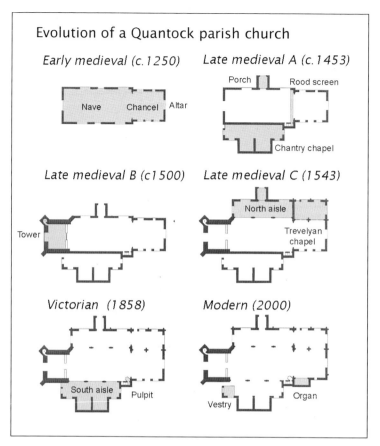

Evolution of a Quantock parish church

Early medieval (c.1250)

Nave Chancel Altar

Late medieval A (c.1453)

Porch Rood screen

Chantry chapel

Late medieval B (c1500)

Tower

Late medieval C (1543)

North aisle

Trevelyan chapel

Victorian (1858)

South aisle Pulpit

Modern (2000)

Vestry Organ

Fig. 4.7 The plans of most 'medieval' parish churches have become ever more complex as chancel, aisles, side chapels and porches were added or elaborated about the original box-like structure. The evolving shape of Nettlecombe parish church typifies this process. See also the print in Fig. 5.9 and Plate 11A. Source: Crothers, 2003 (note 13), 5.

altar. Third, a separate chantry chapel, probably with its own priest, along the south side, containing the remains of the Ralegh family.

Changes continued to be made in the late medieval period. The tower was added at the west end of the nave around 1540 (C) and the rood screen may have been removed around this time. By 1540 (D) the Trevelyan family (the new lords of the manor) have added a new North Aisle and a dedicated family chapel to the left of the chancel. Later changes (E) and (F) occur after the medieval period and are included for completeness. They involve the piercing of the south wall to integrate the chantry chapel as a South Aisle and the addition of an organ space and a small vestry. The sequence of stages shows a pattern of accretion and change, at the behest of the lords of the manor, which has resulted in the typical multi-phase church you see today.

Although many parish churches tend to be an accretion of different building

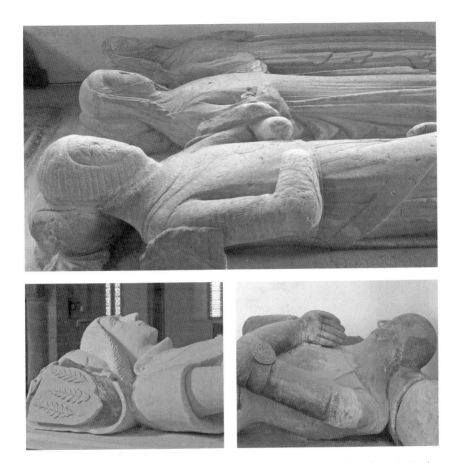

Fig. 4.8 Rare glimpses of Quantock's medieval land owners are provided through the legacy of the stone carvers' art in church memorials. (Above) St John de Meriet of Hestercombe (died 1327) and his two wives Mary and Elizabeth in the parish church of St Peter and St Paul at Combe Florey. (Lower left) John de Verney who with his grandfather William de Verney (died 1333) in the Fairfield Chapel of the Priory Church of St Andrew at Stogursey. (Lower right) A late thirteenth-century Ralegh effigy in the parish church of St Mary the Virgin at Nettlecombe.

phases, occasionally one style is dominant. Church fabrics from the twelfth century dominate Cothelstone, Bicknoller and Broomfield churches. Good examples of fourteenth-century styles are Crowcombe, Enmore and Over Stowey, while West Bagborough and Kingston St Mary are largely from the next century. From the variety and richness a few churches stand out: Bishops Lydeard with its 1450 tower among the best of the Taunton group (Plate 8B), Crowcombe with its superb Perpendicular composition; Kingston St Mary with its 'perfect tower', Stogumber with its Tudor windows, and Stogursey with cruciform Norman structure.

Although many church interiors were modified by Victorian 'improvers' (see Chapter 6), a few retain their medieval memorials. Most moving are the carved faces of local landowning families, typically with the lord of the manor recumbent and armoured, often with a wife or wives at his side and a loyal dog for a foot rest. Fig. 4.8 gives some outstanding examples. The period ended with a final flourish with the introduction of magnificently carved church benchends from 1550, a movement illustrated in Chapter 1 (Fig. 1.7). With this the great period of church building in the Quantocks came to an end. The next generations would put their investment into country houses rather than churches: it was to be the Victorian period before wholly new churches were next to be built here.

Monastic foundations

In parallel to the ubiquitous parish church were a few medieval religious foundations that were different in origin and purpose. Cleeve Abbey is the jewel in the crown but there were other minor monastic buildings, a few of which survive to enrich the region today.[14]

Embracing service to God though prayer and meditation in a community isolated from the rest of society had its origins in the sixth-century model set up by St Benedict at Monte Cassino, Italy. Benedictines came to England in the ninth century and in Somerset established one of their greatest monastic communities, Glastonbury Abbey, in 943. One of several reformed monastic orders was the Cistercians (the 'white' monks) founded at Cîteaux in Burgundy in 1098. Their austere ideal was to return to Benedict's original simplicity, often by finding a remote location for their community where (in addition to prayer

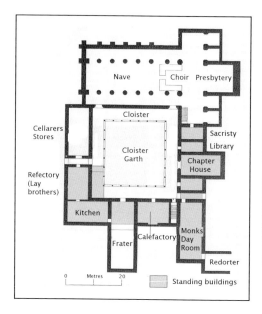

Fig. 4.9 Plan of Cleeve Abbey with (right) *the gatehouse. Source: Adkins & Adkins, 1992 (note 15), 42.*

and meditation) they could undertake the hard physical labour of cultivation of waste land. The first Cistercian house was established in England in 1128 and by the end of the century over one hundred followed. One of these was in the far west of Quantock country in the Washford valley (the romantically-named Vallis Florida, 'valley of the flowers') to the south of the village of Old Cleeve. Dedicated to the Virgin Mary, it was founded in 1198 by the lord of the manor, William Earl of Roumane, as a daughter community from a Lincolnshire abbey.

Cleeve Abbey was to survive as a medieval monastic community for more than three hundred years. Over this period its fortunes fluctuated, prospering in its first century (by 1297 there were 26 monks), declining in the fourteenth century, and recovering somewhat thereafter. It was closed along with other Somerset monasteries in 1537 as part of Henry VIII's dissolution and the remaining seventeen monks pensioned off.

The extensive buildings which made up the monastery are mapped in Fig. 4.9.[15] The church was the centre of the monk's life of prayer in the monastery. That at Cleeve was built in the early thirteenth century with Henry III recorded as giving oak from Newton Park (near Bath) to make the choir stalls. Although only the footings of the walls and pillars remain, the dimensions and cruciform pattern show a building larger (180 feet from West door to high altar and 100 feet from North to South Transept) than the grandest Quantock parish church.

To the south of the abbey church, the residential buildings for living and working formed a rectangular quadrangle or cloister. On the west were a range of buildings for the lay brothers facing on the east a two storey set of buildings. Below lay the sacristy, library, chapter house, parlour and working day room; above, the sleeping quarters with a staircase allowing the monks direct access into the south transept of the church for night-time services. Today, visitors enter the abbey from the nearby car park via the impressive two-storey gatehouse lying north of the monastic complex (Plate 9). Although the gatehouse is thirteenth-century in origin, it has been much reinforced against subsidence by later additions and may have been rebuilt in the early sixteenth century. A Latin inscription above the arch, which translates as 'gate be open, shut to no honest man' was probably added at this period. The gatehouse is flanked on the ground floor by a porter's lodge and almonry and has a high-status room on the upper floor which may have been used as a manorial court.

Dissolution of the Cleeve community in 1537 is beautifully captured in a poem by Berta Lawrence, *Exit from Cleeve*:[16]

> Early morning smelling of new-mown grass
> In silence they pass through the gatehouse,
> Thirty men in white homespun,
> Heads bowed and hands in sleeves.

The gatehouse is inscribed 'Closed to no honest man'.
But to them it is closed forever.
One last look towards the cloister,
Then for the last time they cross the garth,
Stand in the lane and hear once more
The shallow prattle of the Roadwater
Running down their Vallis Florida
Between the buttercups and mallows.

Never again will they climb the narrow stair
To eat beneath bent angel-heads
Sweetly smiling between their carven curls,
Never again tread that chill tiled floor
Blazoned with arms of Charlemagne and Lion Heart.

Now they stand in the stony Washford lane,
Eyes turned towards the Brendon Hills
And on their flocks at pasture.

After dissolution, the local community had no need for such a large church. It was probably demolished and its valuable timber and building stone re-used. But the remaining abbey buildings, though neglected, had use as farm outbuildings and survived. In the late Victorian period George Luttrell of nearby Dunster Castle purchased the ruins of the old abbey and used his estate workers to repair some buildings and excavate others. In 1951 the site passed into the care of the Ministry of Works (now English Heritage) and is today open to the public.

If Cleeve Abbey is the greatest symbol of medieval monasticism in the Quantocks then Kilve Priory (Fig. 4.10) can lay claim to second place. It stands today somewhat forlornly near the parish church, its ruined walls propped up by English Heritage scaffolding and adjacent to a medieval farm (seat of a favourite tea garden) which is itself of considerable historical interest. Although known as Kilve Priory, the building was established in 1329 by Simon de Furneaux as a chantry.[17] Lands were given to maintain a small college of five priests to pray for his soul and those of his family. The ruined portion which survives appears to have had a solar and first-floor chapel. The chantry did not survive long and by 1411 appears to have been used as a farm building. In 1848 the eastern part of the adjacent manor house burnt down: inflammable casks of spirits, probably smuggled ashore from Kilve Pill, are said to have intensified the fire.

Not all symbols of the medieval church are as striking and separate as Cleeve and Kilve. Ruins of other buildings stand hidden, below bramble thickets or behind walls. At Adscombe near Over Stowey, footings of a thirteenth century chapel dedicated to the Virgin Mary survive. A favoured haunt of the poet

Fig. 4.10 Complex of buildings around Kilve church. Watercolour and bodycolour by W. W. Wheatley, 1847, of the parish church, manor and priory labelled 'St Mary's Church, Kilve, and Kilve Abbey'. Photograph (upper right) *of the remains of the manor house and priory today looking north from the churchyard. Source: Wheatley illustration is from the Braikenridge Collection in the Somerset Archaeological and Natural History Society archives.*

Coleridge, it was probably built by the monks of Athelney Abbey who had an estate here. The high garden walls of Cannington Farm Institute abut the site of a Benedictine nunnery founded around 1138 which also served as refuge for ladies from prominent Somerset families.[18] An inquiry in 1351 suggested some worldliness with nuns accused of outside liaisons. It was dissolved in 1536 with its site and accompanying lands granted to Sir Edward Rogers who converted the building into the Court House.

At Stogursey, only a rebuilt circular dovecot on Priory Farm marks the former existence of another priory. It was established by Lonlay Abbey in Normandy but an enquiry of 1326 found it had been reduced to 'one spend-thrift French prior, one monk, servants and useless folk'.[19] War with France led to a confiscation of the priory and its lands and its transfer to Eton College. The substantial prior's house was demolished in 1810 and the Eton estate sold off in 1921. The priory at Ash Priors in the southwest of the region survives only in the village name and a house called the Priory.

Still other forms of medieval orders have left no obvious sign in the landscape today. Knights Templar and Knights Hospitaller were military in nature (formed at the time of the Crusades to protect the Holy Sepulchre and Christian pilgrims to the Holy Land) with members bound by monastic vows and given land in the Quantocks to support their cause. Land at Tolland in the Brendon

Hills was given for the support of the hospitallers by Ralph, son of William, about 1180 and the knights of the order nominated rectors until 1539. At nearby Elworthy, the patronage of the church was also held by the Knights Hospitaller from 1233 until the extinction of the order in 1540. The rectory estate of the small parish of Durleigh was held by St John's Hospital, Bridgwater, up until the Reformation.[20]

THE MEDIEVAL ECONOMY

The wealth that lay behind the surge in church building and re-building in the middle and later part of the medieval period came from the land. We look here at the medieval manor and its agriculture, the pattern of local trading through markets and fairs, the roads which allowed transport of goods and the industries which processed local resources.[21]

Medieval manors and farming

Landowning names recorded in Domesday (Fig. 4.1) and the grand monuments in local churches (Fig. 4.8) are memorials to some of the families who as lords of Quantock manors controlled the use of land in the region.[22] We are lucky in the number of fine medieval manor houses that have survived. The richest and largest of these were rebuilt and incorporated into the grand structures of country houses (discussed in the next chapter). But others survive in more or

Fig. 4.11 The Quantock region is rich in medieval manor houses. Blackmore Farm, Cannington, was probably built by Thomas Tremayll in the late fifteenth century and is replete with a solar and medieval chapel (right).

less their original form and remain, with their halls and small family chapels, as medieval memorials today. Two, near Cannington, are among the finest survivals and have the added advantage that the visitor can stay in both. [23]

Blackmore Farm (Fig. 4.11) is still the heart of a working farm today. It is built of local red sandstone with a main hall range, bedrooms with curved windbraces, and a small chapel projecting forward at its north end. It was rebuilt in the late fifteenth century by Thomas Tremayll who made his profits both from local sheep farming and from practising law in London. Just a mile to the east is Gurney Street Manor, with its buildings arranged around four sides of a court-yard with wings protruding from a further shallow courtyard at the north front. It includes a solar and small chapel. Named after a local family, the Gurneys, who held land in the area in the fourteenth century, the house was remodelled between 1503 and 1539 by Thomas Michell ' a man of great possessions'. It was lovingly restored by the Landmark Trust and is now divided into flats. Other early manor houses survive at Stringston (Parsonage Farm), Dodington (Dodington Hall), Sampford Brett (Aller Farm), Old Cleeve (Bincombe Farm) and Tolland (Gaulden Manor).

We know relatively little in detail of the kind of farming which was conducted to fill the barns and bellies of the manors and their inhabitants. The familiar schoolboy model of medieval farming with three 'rotating' open fields divided into individual strips, was not dominant in the Quantocks. The defini-tive source, the topographic volumes of the *Victoria County History*, covers only two-thirds of the region. Seven of the 30 parishes studied so far have no records of open-field agriculture. For the others, contemporary documents confirm open fields around Watchet, Williton and Doniford in St Decuman's parish (1288), at Rodway in Cannington and Holford (1301), at Crowcombe (1352), and at Tuxwell manor in Spaxton (1540). A fourteenth century inquisition for Crowcombe notes '80 acres of arable land of which two parts are tillable...and the third part...in the common fallow'. [24] But in others the process of consoli-dation of strips into larger holdings had already begun as in the case of Nether Stowey by the fifteenth century. In others the open fields continued beyond the medieval period and in a few places such as Crowcombe and the coastal parishes of Kilton and Lilstock it lasted in a modified form into the mid-nineteenth century to show up on tithe maps (Fig. 4.12).

A glimpse of agricultural practices of a Quantock manor in the fourteenth century is given in a manuscript preserved at Wells. [25] Bicknoller manor at this time records twelve freeholders, eight villeins, seven lesser 'villani', and seven cottars and the transcript sets out in detail each man' s jobs and the number of days to be spent on each job. The work included ploughing for winter seed and spring corn, harrowing, mowing, 'turning, tossing and lifting the grass', carrying hay with oxen and wain, making the rick, reaping, mowing, and carting. The

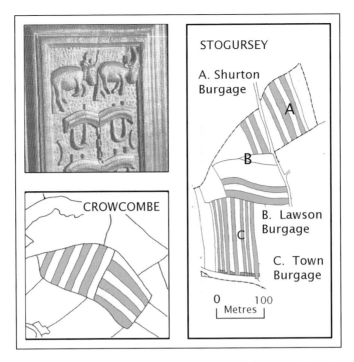

Fig. 4.12 Open fields and medieval strip farming occurred in only some of the Quantock parishes.
(Upper left) *Yoked pairs of oxen provided the energy for strip ploughing as shown on this sixteenth century benchend from Kingston St Mary parish church in the south of the Quantocks.*
(Right) *The remnants of three open fields at Stogursey as shown on a borough plan of 1795.*
(Lower left) *Strips and two open fields at Crowcombe as shown on the 1842 tithe map. Sources: Stogursey plan based on research by M.C. Siraut and R.W. Dunning in Dunning, 1992 (note 9), 133; the Tithe Map of Crowcombe is lodged in the Somerset Heritage Centre, Taunton.*

more menial jobs included scouring the ox-pool, and driving the lord's cattle fourscore leagues (whether to distant pastures or to market or fair is not stated). Each of the villeins appears to have had a smallholding, but details of only the lord's demesne are given.

Medieval farming in the area kept a careful eye on what would today be called 'conservation' practices. A fourteenth century dispute at Bishops Lydeard is recorded in which the parson is censured for over- burdening the lord's ox pasture with too many of his cattle. The high value of the meadowland reflects likewise the limiting factor of winter feed and fourteenth century accounts show that many cattle were killed and salted down in the Autumn.

We showed in Fig. 3.8 that by the eleventh century every major village and many hamlets in our area were in existence. But if we compare their distribution shown in eighteenth-century topographic maps, there still remain a formidable number of hamlets and farmsteads which must have been added after the Norman conquest. When did this secondary colonization of outlying farms and hamlets occur? Evidence from available documents (particularly calendars of inquisitions and farm deeds) show that the first mention of many of the farmsteads occurs in the centuries immediately following the Conquest. Typical is the case of Bishpool Farm in Bishops Lydeard parish, created by a grant of land in 1367. The farm was founded on the eastern side of the Quantock ridge at an elevation of 600 ft. It had rights to cut and burn brushwood, to pasture beasts on 'the hill' (presumably Lydeard Hill, 1,200 feet) and pannage for a score of swine. The remaining demesne woodland was retained by the bishop.[26]

In most cases however, no details of the actual foundation are given, and the first mention of a farm is when it is already in existence. Even when no documentary evidence is available, the pattern of small isolated farms in twos and threes surrounded by small irregular fields with massive hedgebanks, is characteristic of secondary settlement and enclosure from the woodland. It is found particularly on the poorer uplands and hill slopes, and resembles a type which W. G. Hoskins has suggested for Devon is of thirteenth and fourteenth century origin.

Not all the extension was through the founding of new farmsteads; some enclosure from the waste came by the expansion of earlier settlements. With a growing population, more tillable land was needed to feed the new mouths and encroachments on the waste and woodland (called 'assarts') were common. In 1341 a 'piece of waste on Centok' was the subject of dispute between the Lord of West Bagborough and the bishop, who claims it as part of Bishops Lydeard. A compromise was reached whereby the bishop can 'year by year enclose the said waste, breaking it up, cultivating it, and taking other profits; but the lord and tenants of West Bagborough reserve the right of common of pasture all the year round in lands not cultivated, and 'in lands cultivated, after the corn is carried'. The transcript ends with a comment which may well be symptomatic of a contemporary trend, viz. 'every free tenant of the neighbourhood causes the enclosed waste of another to be depastured'.

Markets and fairs

If farming was the fulcrum on which the medieval wealth of the Quantocks rested, then it was one held in place by a series of other essential enterprises: local trading through markets and fairs, roads which allowed transport of goods, and industries which processed local resources.

To hold a weekly market and thus benefit from market tolls, a manorial lord had to establish either a legal right or obtain a market charter from the King. Most major Quantock villages in the medieval period had markets, mostly established in the period of steady economic development in the twelfth and thirteenth centuries (see Fig. 4.13). Records of markets being established include Crowcombe (1227), Bishops Lydeard (1291), Broomfield (1259),

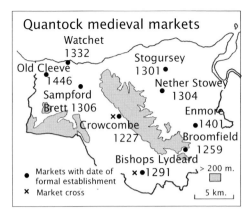

Fig. 4.13 Distribution map of medieval markets and fairs (left). *The heavily-weathered market cross at Crowcombe* (right) *recalls the time when the village was a borough and the cross was the centre of a regular market.*

Stogursey (1301), Nether Stowey (1304), Sampford Brett (1306), Watchet (1332), Enmore (1401) and Old Cleeve (1446). Probably informal markets were already in existence before these dates and market charters simply tidied up existing practice. Market days were carefully arranged not to locally overlap (e.g. Bishops Lydeard on Monday, Crowcombe on Wednesday) and so allow traders and pedlars to move from one to the other. Where villages held markets on the same weekday (e.g. Bishops Lydeard, and Sampford Brett on a Monday) they were sufficiently far apart (in this case, ten miles) to avoid competition.[27]

While no medieval markets have survived intact to the present, the record of early markets can be seen in the present landscape. A market cross was often built at the time of the grant, usually with steps at the base to enhance its dignity and allow wares to be set out. Bishops Lydeard churchyard has the remains of an old market cross (with three octagonal steps and the remains of a shaft); it once stood in the village but was moved to the churchyard in the nineteenth century. Crowcombe has a fourteenth-century cross west of the church. A second less-obvious legacy can be seen in the village plan. Originally, small markets were held around the church but as this was banned so special open market spaces were created (as in Stogursey),

The fair was a kind of 'super' market held annually around a Saint's day but lasting several days and attracting traders from twenty or more miles around. Cattle, sheep and horses were the staple commodities traded but pedlars' goods were also important. While some fairs in England may go back to Saxon times, Moore's *Fairs of Medieval England*[28] suggests that (like markets) the period between the Norman conquest and the Black Death was one in which most were created. By the end of the medieval period Somerset had 150 fairs and several of these were held in the Quantock villages. Crowcombe's annual fair was established by Godfrey of Crowcombe as early as 1227 while Bishops Lydeard had two six-day fairs granted by Edward I in 1291. Broomfield's fair dates from 1259, with Stogursey (1301) and Nether Stowey (1304) following shortly. Nether Stowey's was to last into the nineteenth century. As with markets, dates of fairs were staggered to avoid clashes and held at different times of the year: Stogursey's on St Andrew's day (the patronal festival of the church), Enmore at midsummer, Nether Stowey in early September and Broomfield in early November.

Communication by water in medieval times was critical and it is hard to overstate the key role of small ports like Watchet, Combwich and Bridgwater in the medieval economy of the Quantocks. Away from the coast and rivers, overland movement was difficult and costly. Local paths zig-zagged from one village to the next, edging their way along field boundaries. The ridge of the Quantock Hills provided a corridor rather than barrier and the Saxon routes (shown in Fig. 1.6) continued to be used for longer-distance movement of stock to market. An eighteenth-century estate map hanging in the Court House at East Quantoxhead shows the road to Taunton still following this route. A parallel north-south route skirted the lower slopes of the Quantocks on the west running above Bicknoller (itself a planned Norman settlement) following the contour through old settlements like Halsway, Triscombe, Bagborough and Cothelstone.

As the long-distance routes developed so the opportunities for local services for travellers flourished; the origin and role of Quantock taverns deserves more research. Archivist Mary Siraut suggests the one at Aley Green on the Nether Stowey – Taunton road may be an early example of such a wayside enterprise. We know it was there in 1201 because court records mention that one Geoffrey de Malecombe was murdered when returning from it.[29] We have no surveys of Somerset inns until beyond our period, 1686. That showed Bishops Lydeard with 60 guest beds (and stabling for 48 horses), followed by Stogumber 29 (15), Nether Stowey 15 (16), Watchet 15 (15), Williton 13 (6), and Stogursey 11 (7).[30]

The rise of Quantock industry

As in the Domesday record, mills continued to be at the heart of local industry with sources of water-power widely scattered over the region. Fig. 4.14 shows a typical example. But it was wool and its manufacture into cloth which was the main generator of wealth and employment over much of Wessex. In the Quantocks the shape of the industry's rise is difficult to trace. Sheep were the main stock animal mentioned in Domesday and by the thirteenth century Bridgwater, Taunton and the smaller towns of Taunton Deane had risen to be centres of the cloth industry. Local wool from the Quantock parishes was added to the long-wool of Taunton Deane. Mention of sheep is common in fifteenth century documents and bequests of sheep figure prominently in sixteenth century wills. In 1530, for example, Robert Morell of Cothelstone left 'ryk of

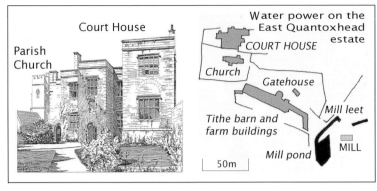

Fig. 4.14 Water power was the key to medieval industry: the mill pond at East Quantoxhead built to power mills on the Lutrell estate. (Upper left) *The Court House with the adjacent parish church.* (Upper right) *Plan of the main estate buildings.* (Below) *View today across the millpond looking north. Source: Sketch by R.W. Paul,* The Builder, *April 1902.*

hay, 4 kyne, 4 calwys, 3 bushells of wite, 2 of rye, 16 of barley, 20 of oats and sheep to everyone'.[31]

By this late medieval period cloth manufacture would seem to have changed its local distribution, for while the main towns around the Quantocks were 'occupied, maintained, and upholden for the most part by reason of the making of woolen cloth' cloth-making also seems to have spread out to the smaller settlements. An appeal is made in 1555 'against people in village and hamlet, not being prentices, who have of late days exercised and occupied the mysteries of cloth making, weaving, fulling, and shearing within their own houses'. The Muster Rolls of 1569 record a number of Fullers, Tuckers and Weavers among the local Quantock surnames, and field names on seventeenth and nineteenth century maps show a high proportion of names suggesting activity connected with cloth manufacturing.

What evidence of the wool and cloth industry can be found in the Quantocks today? First, the richness of the churches. The burst of medieval building and rebuilding could not have occurred without local wealth, surplus capital which can only have come from the profits of the wool trade. When benches started to be placed in churches in the sixteenth century and the bench ends were decorated, it was not surprising that the cloth trade should be honoured in them. Second, the differentiation of the villages. Those that were successful clothmaking centres forged ahead in population and wealth while those wholly dependent on farming alone and with none of the benefits which flowed from adding value through processing, fell behind. Many were never to catch up in later periods.

Research by Ashford suggests that the western part of the county was a much more important part of Somerset's late medieval cloth industry than previously thought.[32] Sheep numbers on Exmoor and the Quantocks were not large enough to supply the local industry and wool bales were imported from Wales and Ireland through local ports such as Bridgwater and Minehead. Even Combwich records two stones of Irish wool arriving in 1529. Dye for colouring the cloth was brought into Bridgwater and Watchet from as far away as Portugal. Export of finished cloth was not only by local shipping to Bristol but as far as Spain with San Sebastian on its north coast as the main importing centre. Cloths known as 'Watchets' were being traded from 1500 and records show cloth originating in the Quantock region having travelled as far as Morocco and the Guinea coast.

One feature of the sixteenth century was the migration of the industry out from the towns of Bridgwater and Taunton into the surrounding villages. Study of occupational names suggest that Stogursey and Stogumber were leading centres for the industry but two thirds of the parishes appeared to have some activity. The Wolcott family of Tolland in the Brendons built up considerable wealth from the clothing industry, expanding their operations into nearby Stogumber, Bishops Lydeard and Lydeard St Lawrence and buying shares in trading vessels from local ports.[33] The Wyndham family of St Decuman's also had a major stake in the local industry. Tucking or fulling mills were widely distributed through the Quantocks with more than twelve locations well documented.

If clothmaking was the dominant small industry it was not the only one. Exploitation of iron resources is recorded in Domesday with the iron slabs paid by tenants at Lexworthy in Spaxton and iron rents recorded in Over Stowey in the late thirteenth century. Court records for the medieval period give occasional glimpses of other industries. At Fairfield manor court in 1386 a Robert Wilcocks of Stogursey, a potter, comes before the Fairfield manor court on a charge. Four miscreants appear at the Durborough manor court in 1446 for leaving open clay pits after their digging and one John Webber (a clothing-industry surname) was 'arrested for selling pots gainst the custom of the manor'.[34] Webber seems unrepentant for he is before the same court again in 1446 breaking rules in the same potting business.

POPULATION AND THE BLACK DEATH

Since regular censuses of population did not begin until 1801, estimates of population over the five centuries that make up the Middle Ages are problematic. We have a rough marker at the start of the period from the Domesday survey of 1086 (discussed at the start of this chapter.) If we add up the returns for the Quantock settlements recorded there these give a total of 950 people (villagers 47 percent, smallholders 36, and slaves 17). If we assume that each enumerated person was the head of a family then we need to allow for them. Assuming a multiplier (say at least 3.5), then we can make the rough estimate that our part of Somerset had a population in the late eleventh century of 950 x >3.5 = >3,300, or in round terms between three to four thousand souls of all ages. There are arguments to be

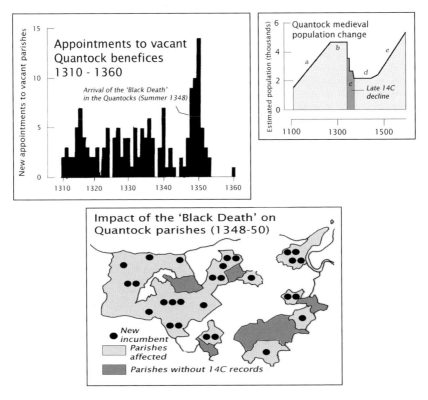

Fig. 4.15 Population change in the Quantocks over the medieval period. (Upper left) Graph of vicar's dates of appointments in the Quantock parishes during the period 1310–1360. Note the peak around 1350. (Upper right) Main phases of population change: see discussion in text. (Lower) Impact of the Black Death (1348–50) on the Quantock parishes. Source: Data from Weaver, 1889 (note 35). Population graph from Simmons, 2001 (note 9), 116.

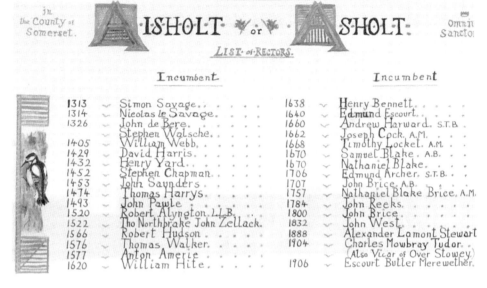

in the County of Somerset.

A·ISHOLT· ⚘ or ⚘ ·SHOLT· Omnium Sanctorum

LIST· of ·RECTORS·

Incumbent		Incumbent	
1313	Simon Savage.	1638	Henry Bennett.
1314	Nicolas le Savage.	1640	Edmund Escourt.
1326	John de Bere.	1660	Andrew Harward. S.T.B
	Stephen Walsche.	1662	Joseph Cock. A.M.
1405	William Webb.	1668	Timothy Locket. A.M
1429	David Harris.	1670	Samuel Blake. A.B.
1432	Henry Yard.	1670	Nathaniel Blake.
1452	Stephen Chapman.	1706	Edmund Archer. S.T.B.
1453	John Saunders.	1707	John Brice. A.B.
1474	Thomas Harrys.	1757	Nathaniel Blake Brice. A.M.
1493	John Pawle.	1784	John Reeks.
1520	Robert Alyngton. LL.B.	1800	John Brice.
1522	Tho Northbrake John Zellack.	1832	John West.
1566	Robert Hudson.	1888	Alexander Lamont Stewart
1576	Thomas Walker.	1904	Charles Mowbray Tudor.
1577	Anton Amerie.		(Also Vicar of Over Stowey.)
1620	William Hite.	1906	Escourt Butler Merewether.

Fig. 4.16 The lists of incumbents that hang in most Quantock parish churches can sometimes throw unexpected light on the demography of the region. Here the remote parish church of Aisholt (see Plate 8A) records the appointment of 33 rectors between 1313 and 1906. As the first graph in Fig. 4.15 shows, many Quantock parishes made new appointments in the Black Death period (1348–50) when nearly one half of Somerset incumbents had to be replaced. Aisholt appears to have escaped but Stephen Walsche's appointment is mysteriously undated.

made that villages in the Taunton Deane part of the region are underestimated by being included in the Bishop of Winchester's great manor at Taunton but even if some adjustment is made for this the total remains under 5,000.

This matches a rough estimate of 4,400 based on the 'Quantock share' of an England-wide Domesday total of 1.75 million.[35] Using a similar 'proportional share' approach the Quantock region may have grown to 10–20,000 by 1340 (Poll Tax evidence), dropped to 5,300 by 1430 (Inquests Post-Mortem), and recovered to 10,300 by 1603 (Ecclesiastical Census). Fig. 4.15 shows these changes as a graph. What is clear from local records is that this part of Somerset did not escape the ravages of the Black Death, the bubonic plague epidemic introduced into England via the Dorset port of Melcombe in June 1348.[36] Although accurate estimates are hard to make, one third of England's population probably died over the next two years.

One clue to the Black Death's local impact in the Quantocks can be teased from the framed list of incumbent parish priests posted on most parish churches by the south door entrance (Fig. 4.16). Data from the fourteenth century are available for 33 of the Quantock parishes (see Fig. 4.15) and of these nearly one half record a priest being replaced in either 1349 or the immediately following year.[37] While the reasons for the sudden peak in priest replacement are not stated, the graph is consistent with other sources suggesting that half the Somerset priests died of the plague during the epidemic. Accordingly, the Quantocks may well have lost one third to one half its population in the mid-fourteenth century.

In the same way that the Devonian laid down the main structure of the Quantock's physical landscape (Chapter 2), so it was that the Medieval period shaped its man-made landscape. By the end of that period the main lineaments of village and hamlet, moorland and cultivated land, roads and lanes had been laid down. As we have seen, the movement was not a uniform one: the early parts of the Middle Ages were generally ones of growth and expansion in a benevolent climatic phase, the middle and later ones of retrenchment and population loss. Although the faults and shocks of the ensuing centuries were to twist and fracture the pattern, much of that medieval pattern remains intact today.

Five

THE EARLY MODERN PERIOD

The years between the ravages of civil war and rebellion in the seventeenth century and the reforms of Church and State that characterized the nineteenth century were a period in which the gentry of Somerset increasingly dominated the countryside.

Robin Bush, *Somerset* (1999).[1]

For a boy educated at a grammar school on the edge of the Quantocks, both parts of the Bush quotation strike a chord. But our civil war was fought as house matches on the rugby field rather than Naseby or Edge Hill. I moved on from my village school at age eleven to study at the local grammar school in Durleigh parish, founded by Dr John Morgan of the Quantock parish of Bishops Lydeard in 1723. On entry, I was allocated to 'Cromwell' house. It was one of the four houses named after a leading Civil War general: Hopton and Wyndham on the Royalist side for boys living west of the River Parrett, Cromwell and Fairfax on the Parliamentary side for those living east of the river.

I was also aware of the role of the Quantock landed gentry on school life. The massive three-dimensional model map of Somerset which lit an early interest in geography (and eventually took me to Cambridge) was a gift of the Wyndham family, lords of the manor at Orchard Wyndham. Special lectures which opened our eyes to Somerset and its history were funded from the same family foundation. When inter-house cups were awarded at the end of the school year, the Quantock's landowning past emerged again. For the man presenting the prizes in my time was the kindly figure of Lord St Audries, chairman of the school's Board of Governors. Here was a man whose title commemorated one Quantock parish (St Audries or West Quantoxhead) but whose family home was the great Tudor country house of Fairfield in another Quantock parish, Stogursey. He was a descendant of the Verney and Acland Hood family who held their estates by direct descent from the twelfth-century Goslan.

In this chapter, I look at the evolution of the Quantocks in the early-modern age. It spans roughly two centuries from the end of the medieval period at around 1550 to the middle and later decades of the eighteenth century. It was a period of rapid change when the foundations for the still greater changes of the Victorian age were laid, not modernization perhaps but its presage. We look first at the period of turbulence that began in late Tudor times, ran through the Civil War and lasted until the Monmouth Rebellion in 1685. What impact did it have locally and what, if any, legacies did it leave? We then turn to one of the grand themes in Quantock history: the emergence of the landed families, the fine country houses they built, and the surrounding estates that remain to grace the landscape today. If the medieval period was a phase of great church building in the Quantocks, the early-modern was one of great house building. In the third section, we look at the economy that powered many of these changes in the landscape: the rise of agriculture and the emergence of rural industries. As activity increased, so the pressures grew on local transport and we look at the plight of local roads and the turnpike solution proposed to solve the problem. Finally, we look at what happened to the overall Quantock population over this period. Did numbers grow or decline and how, in a pre-census age do we know?

TIMES OF INSTABILITY

The first century and a half of the early modern era – covering reigns from Elizabeth through the Commonwealth to Charles II – were years of considerable turbulence in England, an instability from which even the relatively remote Quantock region was not immune. We look in turn at the impact of foreign invasion threats during the late Tudor period, the Civil War of 1642-51, and the Monmouth Rebellion of 1685.

Beacons and foreign threats

One of the commanding points on the northern Quantocks which can be seen from all along the West Somerset coast is Beacon Hill. The name is significant since it was one of the hill tops used both for keeping watch and giving warning by signal fires, possibly from prehistoric times onwards.[2] Beacon Hill was one of a chain of hilltops spaced a mile or so apart which stretched south and east from the coast at Cleeve Hill down along the ridge of the Quantock Hills to Cothelstone Beacon overlooking Taunton. In the Elizabethan period when wars against Spain and France were threatening, a sophisticated warning system was in full operation. No detailed description of the Quantock beacons survive but a late-eighteenth century account describes the remains at Dunkery Beacon on Exmoor with 'three large fire-hearths about eight feet square and built of rough unwrought stones…the fire-places form an equilateral triangle'. Others had three braziers or iron tripods with a store of combustible material kept at hand.

The Elizabethan warning system was under the control of the local Justices of the Peace. They authorized the lighting and guarded against the confusion that could arise from false alarms. The signal code was three stage: one fire a preliminary warning of danger, two to confirm that invasion was imminent, and three to signal the enemy had landed. Evidence has survived from the Hundred of Williton and Freemanors, of preparations for defence against a possible French landing in 1555.

The beacons were only useful if backed up by some system of local defence, an Elizabethan equivalent to the US National Guard or our own Home Guard in World War II. In 1547 an order was issued throughout the whole country 'to have ready a good number of able horse and foot, either for the annoyance of our enemies or the defence of the realm'. Owners of large estates had to provide horses, horsemen and equipment for fighting, with numbers varying by size of their estate. Commissioners were appointed for each county (those for Somerset included Sir John Wyndham of Orchard Wyndham near Williton) to prepare lists of able men ready to be trained to fight. Coastal defences were prepared with Watchet as one of the places specially protected with trenches and parapets. Unlike Bridgwater (which despatched the *William*) it was not large enough to need to send a vessel to join Drake's fleet at Plymouth.

In the event, the Spanish invasion did not materialize and Quantock men were sent south to reinforce their Dorset colleagues as the Armada moved up the English Channel. It was to be more than two centuries before Revolution in France and the Napoleonic threat rekindled interest in the hill beacon system. But the 'local muster' system had its legacy in the Yeomanry regiments and Home Guard which played a part in the more recent conflicts.

Civil war

The nine years of the English Civil War (1642-51) touched Quantock country only obliquely and only in the first phase of that long nine-year conflict.[3] Movements of the main Royalist army in 1644 and the New Model Army under Fairfax in 1645 were confined to the east of Somerset. No major battles were fought in the Quantocks, though those at Isle Moors and Burrowbridge and the sieges of Dunster, Taunton, and Bridgwater (twice) that occurred between 1643 and 1645 were nearby.

But in other ways, the Quantocks played its part, albeit in a minor key, and could not avoid its share of pain. A skirmish at Over Stowey in 1645 was typical: there the Selleck family fortified the church tower and parsonage and rang bells to summon the villagers to oppose a Roundhead attack from Taunton in which 'many soldiers and commanders were slain'.

Fig. 5.1 The manor house at Cothelstone in the southern Quantocks was one of the estates badly affected by the Civil War and by reported hangings after the Monmouth Rebellion (1685).

Leading land-owning families such as the Wyndhams were generally Royalist in sympathy and paid the penalty as a result during the Commonwealth. None illustrates this more keenly than Sir John Stawell of Cothelstone (Fig. 5.1) to whom the Civil War brought tragedy. He fought for the King from the first Somerset skirmish at Marshalls Elm near Street through to the surrender of Exeter. He was imprisoned in the Tower of London from 1650 for treason and murder and his house at Cothelstone Manor severely damaged.. As late as 1659 it was still being stripped of its lead. Finally released from the Tower, Sir John died in 1662 not at the ruined Cothelstone but at his other Somerset manor house at Low Ham. Not all Royalists were as honourable as Stawell. Sir Francis Dodington of Dodington parish drew infamy during the Civil War for hanging those who surrendered to him and for shooting dead a defenceless priest near Taunton.

Other Quantock houses which suffered damage from occupation by Parliamentary troops were Stowey Court in Nether Stowey and Combe Sydenham in Stogumber parish. In the latter case an 'accommodation', no doubt involving cider, was made when the owner persuaded parliamentary soldiers that a small and token fire (with much smoke) would substitute for burning down the whole house. In other cases, military occupation meant annoyance rather than destruction. The lawyer John Turberville of Tolland wrote in 1647 that his house at Gaulden Manor '…is full of soldiers this fortnight, such uncivil drinkers and thirsty souls that a barrel of good beer trembles at the sight of them, and the whole house nothing but a rendezvous of tobacco and spitting.'[4] Within the established church, some royalist sympathizers were ejected from their livings: Dr John Goodwin from Lydeard St Lawrence and John Selleck from Elworthy in 1645. Selleck was a staunch royalist who personally aided the escape of the future Charles II.

But not all support was on the Royalist side and occasionally (as at Halswell House in Goathurst) it was royalist troops that were billeted on a suspected parliamentary sympathizer. John Venn, whose family held Pyleigh in Lydeard St Lawrence parish was a leading Roundhead colonel during the Civil War, served as governor of Windsor Castle and was a signatory to the death warrant of Charles I. Most important was John Pym who was born on the Cannington estate at Brymore, home of the Pym family from the thirteenth century. Pym was leader of the House of Commons at the outbreak of the Civil War and one of the defiant five members whom Charles I tried to arrest in 1642. His interment in Westminster Abbey did not survive the restoration.

The Monmouth rebellion

Though the Monmouth Rebellion lasted only 26 days and the Battle of Sedgmoor only ninety minutes, the legacy for Somerset and for the Quantocks has been surprisingly persistent.[5] James, Duke of Monmouth, the eldest of Charles II's illegitimate children landed on June 11th 1685 at Lyme on the Dorset coast with three small ships and eighty men. Within a week he had arrived to a rapturous welcome at Taunton and was proclaimed 'King Monmouth'. By now his forces had swollen to three regiments, the largest of 800 men. After two weeks of frustrating movements in east Somerset, his course towards London blocked by the King's forces, he returned to regroup at Bridgwater. The fateful Battle of Sedgemoor on July 5th 1685 was decisively lost with 700 dead rebels against 27 Royalists deaths.

The brief rebellion brought an awful retribution, both through the summary execution of prisoners by Colonel Lamb and the drawn-out judicial slaughter by Judge Jeffreys. Many of the Quantock villages had contributed rebels to Monmouth's cause and now it was their turn to pay. At Nether Stowey, three Monmouth rebels, one from nearby Durleigh, were executed late in 1685. The church register at Stogursey records how Hugh Ashley and John Hirrin were hanged at Tower Hill at the higher end of the village (now the site of the school) before their heads and quarters were displayed around the village.[6] Three rebels from the Taunton area were hanged at Stogumber, traditionally at Heddon Oak on the road to Crowcombe.

Such slaughter did not go without local criticism. Sir Francis Warre of Hestercombe who served as MP for both Taunton and Bridgwater was involved in raising the ransom for the 'Maids of Taunton', girls who had welcomed Monmouth there. Lord Stawell, a member of the Cothelstone family, who had suffered in the Civil War, openly criticized the severity of the Bloody Assizes. As a result Judge Jeffreys ordered two rebels to be executed at Cothelstone though whether, as local tradition says, by hanging from the archway is yet unsupported by archival evidence. It was a final irony that one of those hanged there was a former Roundhead, who had persecuted the Stawells after the Civil War.

There has been considerable debate over the origin of the rebels. Were they drawn from one particular disaffected group or class? John Evelyn stated that '..most of the party were Anabaptists and poor clothworkers'.[7] Dunning's recent review of the surviving documentary evidence suggests they were more widely drawn than their banners 'Fear Nothing But God' suggest. The bulk of support came from the villages of west Dorset and east Devon, but his research suggests that the Quantocks region contributed their fair share, although there are some curious anomalies. There was not a single Monmouth supporter from Watchet (surely not all its able-bodied men were at sea?) and the populous village of Bishops Lydeard made no contribution. In contrast, the small east Quantock village of Durleigh contributed eight rebels. The neighbouring towns also pose questions: Taunton accounted for 393 rebels (nearly half of them cloth workers) but Bridgwater, twice visited by Monmouth, contributed only seventeen.

COUNTRY HOUSES AND THEIR ESTATES

If the medieval church was the iconic symbol of the Quantocks in the middle ages, then the country house took its place in the two centuries which followed. We look here at the rise of the country estate and the handful of landowning families who dominated the region's public and economic life, represented it in

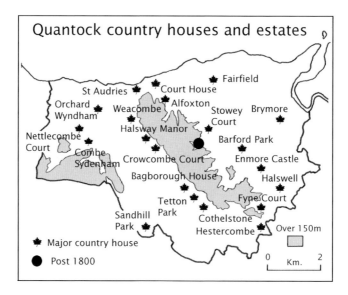

Fig. 5.2 Map of the main country houses and estates ringing the Quantock Hills in the early modern period.

parliament, upheld its laws, led its forces, invested in its economy. The country houses they built and the estates they cultivated (Fig. 5.2), remain today a legacy that gives character to much of the lowland landscape around the Quantock Hills.

Quantock families

As any genealogist will confirm, family history shows up such a tangled skein of interwoven bloodlines that the chances of finding a coherent pattern is low. Typically, a few families in this early modern period rose briefly to public prominence through particularly gifted members but then faded from public notice. The Blakes at Plainsfield produced Robert Blake (1599-1657), one of the most successful of British admirals and a military commander in the English Civil War. The Pyms of Brymore, Cannington, produced the English parliamentarian, John Pym (1584-1643), the leader of the Long Parliament and the only Quantock man to be buried (albeit briefly) in Westminster Abbey.

But from the background choreography of intertwining lines, a few Quantock families stand out who have not only acquired wealth (usually in the form of land) but, a much more difficult task, have husbanded and augmented this across many generations.[8] The two families with the greatest claims to regional longevity are the Luttrells of Dunster and East Quantoxhead and the Acland-Hoods of West Quantoxhead (St Audries) and Stogursey (Fairfield). The Luttrells originated in Normandy and by the twelfth century had extensive estates in the English midlands, particularly Lincolnshire. A branch of the

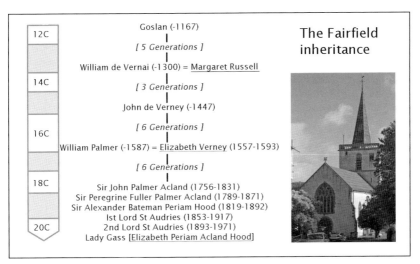

Fig. 5.3 Highly-simplified family tree of a Quantock landowning family, the Verneys of Fairfield House, Stogursey. Some thirty generations separate the original 1167 owner (Goslan of Fairfield) from the present owner (Lady Gass). Memorials of many members of the family can be found in the Verney chapel in the parish church of St Andrew, Stogursey. Source: Adapted from Ballard, 1992 (note 9), 38-39.

family settled in the Quantock area probably around 1250, building and occupying the Court House at East Quantoxhead until the present century. Estate land there has been in continuous ownership for more than seven centuries. An even longer continuity is traceable on the Fairfield estate in Stogursey parish. Here the family name has sometimes changed, from Verney through Palmer, to Acland Hood, but the continuity of family ownership has been retained. A highly-simplified family tree (Fig. 5.3) shows how marriage and backtracking along branches to find new growing points allowed the line to be continued.[9] Over the generations the family provided Members of Parliament, soldiers and admirals, explorers and administrators. The present owner, Lady Gass (Elizabeth Periam Acland Hood) serves today as Lord Lieutenant for Somerset.

Although the time spans are not as long or ownership as continuous, the history of the Luttrell and Acland-Hood families can be paralled by a number of other major landowning families in the area. Cothelstone was held by the Stawell family from 1166 and Nettlecombe by the Trevelyans from the fifteenth century. Marriage brought the Carews to Crowcombe around 1620 and the Wyndhams to Orchard Wyndham (near Williton) and Tyntes to Halswell (near Goathurst) at around the same time. Other familes with long and illustrious Quantock connections include the Malets of Enmore, the Warres of Kingston St Mary, the St Aubyns of Stringston, the Pophams of West Bagborough. In some

Fig. 5.4 Some of the great Quantock families are recalled in dedicated chapels within their local parish churches. Detail (inset) from the Wyndham family chapel in the parish church of St Decuman at Watchet. Sir William Wyndham, Baronet, died in 1683.

cases the incoming families had land in other parts of Somerset (the Stawells and the Tyntes) but more often the links were more distant: the Luttrells with Lincolnshire, the Trevelyans and St Aubyns with Cornwall.

There are two enjoyable ways to see these family connections on the ground today. The first is to visit the local parish church. This was often a creature of the estate: the Lord of the Manor chose the incumbent, endowed the family chapels, and bankrolled church repairs and re-building. At Nettlecombe, the church snuggles up to the big house serving almost as a detached family chapel (Plate 11A). Of the fine examples of family chapels within a parish church, the Wyndham chapel at St Decumans, Watchet (Fig. 5.4) and the Tynte chapel at St Edward, Goathurst (Plate 10) are outstanding in their exhuberance.[10] Less ostentatious family chapels at Crowcombe (for the Carew family) or Stogursey (for the Verney family and their successors) are also worth visiting. A second way to see family connections is to retire from the church to the local tavern. For as we illustrate in Fig. 7.11, pub names with their distinctive heraldic inn signs (such as the 'Tynte Arms' at Enmore) continue to mark longstanding family connections.

Quantock country houses

With increased wealth came the desire to have family houses to reflect that status. In some cases this was achieved by progressive rebuilding of the original dwelling, much in the way that parish churches were rebuilt and extended. Fig.

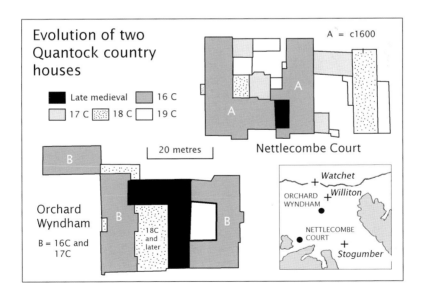

Fig. 5.5 Like parish churches, most Quantock country houses evolved over time. Nettlecombe Court, home of the Trevelyan family (see also Fig. 5.9, and Plate 11A) and Orchard Wyndham, home of the Wyndham family. Source: M.C. Siraut in Dunning, 1985 (note 11), 114, 154.

5.5 gives two examples to illustrate this process.[11] Nettlecombe Hall is a complex house built largely of red sandstone. It consists of a small medieval core around which shells of later age have been added. It was reconstructed by John Trevelyan around 1600 with two courts and a two-storeyed porch. Around 1705 another John Trevelyan (to the confusion of historians there were six Johns in succession) added new ranges and yet a third John completed this in the 1780s to give the house we largely see today. Currently the house is used as the Leonard Wills Field Studies centre. A similar rebuilding process was conducted by successive Wyndhams two miles to the north. In the case of Orchard Wyndham, the original medieval courtyard was supplemented by a second courtyard with hall and family chapel in the Tudor period. Extensive modifications continued in the seventeenth and eighteenth century as new wings were added and old areas refurbished. The house as you see it today with its Victorian bargeboards is a thoroughly English mix of styles and compromises.

While all Quantock houses show later modification, many retain a dominant architectural style from a single period.[12] Fairfield near Stogursey is essentially Elizabethan, probably replacing a fourteenth-century manor house: a chapel was recorded in 1313. The date on the porch on the south-east front is 1589 and the house is modelled on the familiar E-shaped plan. It has a fine collection of mullioned and transomed windows. Although the house we see today was remodelled in 1780 and again in 1815, it retains its Tudor atmosphere. Other houses of this period include Combe Sydenham in Stogumber parish which was remodelled in 1580 by Sir George Sydenham. There are fewer examples for the next century but they include Halswell House in Goathurst regarded by Pevsner as 'the most important house of its date in the county'. The date in question was 1689 when Sir Halswell Tynte added a majestic north front to a house whose roots go back to at least 1318 and which had major rebuilding in 1536.

But it was the eighteenth century which saw the finest examples of country house building in the Quantocks. The list includes my personal favourite, the small but exquisite Barford Park (Fig. 5.6) lying between Enmore and Spaxton. It was built for the Jeanes family around 1710, augmented by a third storey and by flanking wings in 1775. Over the last half-century it has been lovingly preserved by Michael Stancomb. Other houses in order of construction include Alfoxton Park near Holford built for the St Aubyn family (Plate 5A), Sandhill Park near Ash Priors for the Lethbridge family (1720), Crowcombe Court for the Carew family (1725), Thorncombe House for the Sweeting family (1744), Weacombe House near Bicknoller and Terhill House for the Slocombe family (1750), and Fyne Court for the Crosse family (1799). Standing out oddly from this list is Enmore Castle, a pseudo-baronial structure built for the Earl of Egmont near the parish church in 1799.

Fig. 5.6 Barford Park was built around 1710 for the Jeanes family and extended by the addition of a third story and two curving wings in 1775 (see also Fig. 1.11). Over the last sixty years it has been beautifully conserved by the Stancomb family.

Quantock estate parkland

If we look at the Tudor maps for the county of Somerset, we see marked not only the location of the larger estates but also the parkland which was beginning to surround them.[13] For the Quantocks, Speed's 1610 map shows parks around both the Stawell house at Cothelstone and the Luttrell house at East Quantoxhead. Such parks were mainly reserved for herds of deer with an Archdeacon of Wells writing in the seventeenth century that 'almost everywhere a man may see clausures and parks paled and enclosed and fraughts with venerie'. He complains that such parks interfered with tillage and 'almost the third part of the ground is left unmanured either for their harts of their fallow deer or their conies'. Over the next century, surrounding a country seat with parkland and using careful planting and landscaping to enhance its setting were to change the English landscape. Fig. 5.7 shows three examples of Quantock great houses taken from the engravings which accompanied John Collinsons great volume on the *Antiquities*.

Many of the Quantock grounds were modelled on Romantic lines in the eighteenth century. At Halswell, Sir Charles Kemys Tynte created a lake near the house with an ornamental bridge and placed follies at strategic points around the extensive grounds: a rotunda with an ice-house beneath, a stepped pyramid and a temple. The temple has recently been restored (see Plate 12A) and is accessible from the road. But the greatest example of landscaped ground is provided by the Hestercombe estate which lies some two miles south of Halswell on the

Fig. 5.7 Views of three major Quantock country houses drawn by Thomas Bonner to illustrate John Collinson's History and Antiquities of the County of Somerset (1791). (Above) Fairfield, Stogursey. (Centre) Crowcombe Court, Crowcombe. (Below) Halswell House, Goathurst.

southern flank of the Quantocks. The land here was continuously owned by one family, the Warres, for half a millennium from 1391 to 1872.[14] While a plan for designing a landscaped garden was put forward as early as 1731 the garden we see today was that of Coplestone Warre Bampfylde who inherited the estate from his father in 1750 and worked out his ideas for the garden over the next thirty years. The long narrow combe running up to the north of the house was landscaped to mimic the picturesque scenes shown in the paintings of Poussin and Lorrain.

Two essential elements in such landscaping were water and carefully-placed buildings to catch the eye. At Hestercombe the main stream down the combe was dammed to form two elongated lakes, the large Pear Pond in the lower valley and the small Box Pond in the upper valley. Water from the latter was taken off to power a 'Great Cascade' which spilled down the western side of the valley. At intervals around the shoulders of a valley were placed a series of seats and viewpoints and a set of four buildings (the Gothic Alcove, the Temple Arbour, the Witch House, and the Mausoleum) built to catch the eye. Fig. 5.8 gives a contemporary view of the garden which is now open to the public and

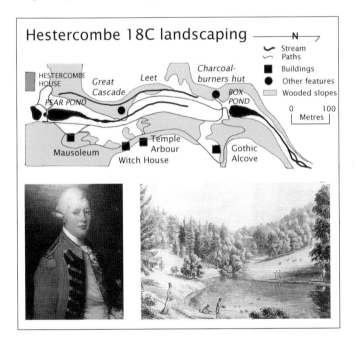

Fig. 5.8 Hestercombe in the southern Quantocks was the scene of a major landscaping enterprise in the 1750s. (Above) Map of the combe running north from Hestercombe House with the main elements in the landscaping plan: ponds, follies and cascades. (Below left) Portrait of Coplestone Warre Bampfylde (1720–1791) who commissioned the garden. (Lower right) Contemporary sketch of 'The Pear Pond, Hestercombe' from the Whitworth Art Gallery, University of Manchester. Sources: Hestercombe Gardens, 2006 (note 14).

is being lovingly restored by the Hestercombe Gardens Trust. Although such folly-building peaked in the eighteenth century, it continued for some years with Cothelstone Beacon and Willett Hill (Plate 12B) providing examples of more modern examples.

THE EARLY-MODERN ECONOMY

Economic changes powered the emergence of the Quantock region in the early modern period. We take in turn, the agricultural, industrial and transport sections of the economy.

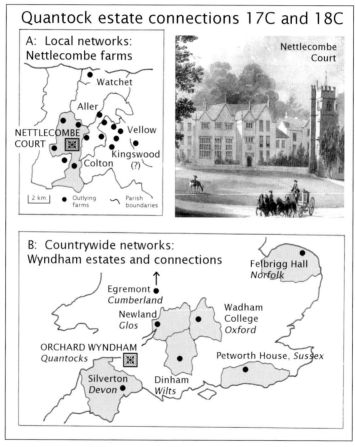

Fig. 5.9 Estates generally covered an area much wider than the great house with its surrounding gardens and park. (Upper left) Map of the Trevelyan estate at Nettlecombe Court in 1619 with the home farm, other holdings in the parish, farms in adjacent parishes, and a town house in Watchet. (Upper right) Print of Nettlecombe Court. (Below) Orchard Wyndham was a small component of a wide range of other Wyndham estates and foundations across the country. Source: The Nettlecombe map is redrawn from Alcock & Carson, 2007 (note 15), 146. The print of Nettlecombe Court is probably eighteenth century but undated and unattributed. See Dunning, 1991 (note 12), 138.

The agricultural economy

In looking at the rise of the great houses and surrounding parkland, we have emphasized the role of a few Quantock landowning families in shaping the region. As Fig. 5.9 shows, the writ of these estates ran much wider than the main house and its landscaped grounds.[15] Most estates were at the centre of a network of outlying farms. Nettlecombe Court records for 1619 show that in addition to the home farm there were fourteen other farms spread over four contiguous adjacent parishes. The figure goes on to show for a second Quantock estate, Orchard Wyndham, that the Somerset estate was one cog in a much larger network of family estates and connections spreading over seven counties. Understanding Orchard Wyndham needs to note that it was part of a family 'empire' that included such great houses of Felbrigg in Norfolk and Petworth in Sussex. Capital needed for investments in Quantock enterprises might draw on profits from other family holdings both in England and even overseas (including the Caribbean and North America).

Social historians sometimes draw a stark contrast at this time between the score of richly manicured Quantock estates and a poor peasant subsistence farming. But if we look at a number of the large farms around the region that have survived from this period, we see some signs of independent wealth. One indicator is provided by a remarkable study by the Penoyres of the decorative plasterwork on Somerset houses between 1500 and 1700. The distribution map in Fig. 5.10 suggests that such conspicuous expenditure was not just confined to the grand houses.[16] Unlike the better known 'pargetting' in East Anglia where decorated plaster was a feature of the outside of houses, here it was confined to the inside: ceilings, friezes and overmantels.

Growth in both population and wealth brought changes in the landscape outside the great estates. Enclosure of waste land brought more of the Quantocks into cultivation. Taking in hill land for pasture is mentioned frequently in Tudor documents with areas in Kingston Combe and Buncombe in Broomfield 'alienated by licence' from the waste. Amounts are small and grants of fifty acres or over appear to be uncommon. Travellers in the region confirm the evidence of early enclosure with John Norden (1607) and Celia Fiennes (1698) citing the county as an examplar: Norden writing of Taunton Deane comments 'that poor men live as well there on twenty pounds a year as elsewhere on a hundred' while Fiennes describes a view of West Somerset: 'full of enclosures...good grass, and corn besett with quicksetts and hedge rows'. Of the poorer hill areas there is little comment by contemporary travellers, but towards the end of the period, the 1733 Court rolls of Crowcombe show that although the 'breaking up and tilling' of the Common had been adjusted to a money rent, further encroachment resulted in fines.[17]

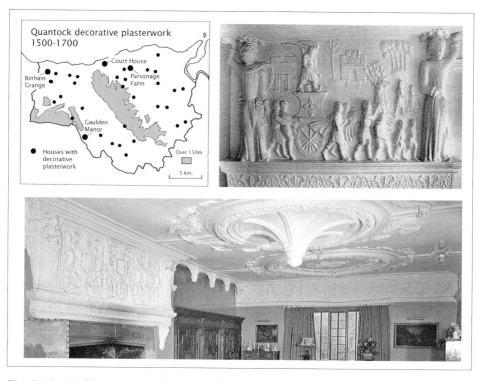

Fig. 5.10 Wealth on Quantock farms and manor houses. (Above left) *Map of houses with decorative plasterwork, 1500–1700.* (Above right) *Decorated plaster overmantel called the 'Triumph of Time' from Binham Farm, Old Cleeve.* (Below) *Decorated ceiling and overmantel at Gaulden Manor, Tolland. Source: Penoyre & Penoyre, 1994 (note 16), 34, 70 and postcard collection.*

By the seventeenth century the medieval manorial system was crumbling and smaller farmers increasingly asserted themselves against the great (but often absent) estate landowners. Mary Siraut has traced a number of such examples of land enclosure in the Quantocks:

> In the 1630s at least 180 acres, part of Plainsfield Hill, was divided and allotted to local landowners including the lord of Plainsfield manor in return for the surrender of their claims to common over the whole area. By 1683, and probably by 1656, about half the remainder of the Stogursey land had been enclosed and let, and Quantock Farm was created soon after 1686.[18]

Outside the bounds of the great estates and the major farms, lay the common land mostly located on the higher and poorer Grade III ground of the Quantock Hills. This was divided into a patchwork of 'parish ownership' much more complex than looking at today's map would suggest. Some parishes abutting the hills (e.g. Over Stowey) had poor access to the hill commons while some further away (e.g. Stogursey) were well placed. As we noted in Chapter 1, the bounds of each parish's holding were carefully laid out with trackways, landmarks and gateways marked and regularly perambulated with the manor court keeping a careful record.

Use of the commons was strictly regulated with rights (e.g. to grazing) carefully specified by Courts of Survey. Breaking the rules would land miscreants in court and thus much of the information at this period comes from court records. Tenants were allowed to break the soil of the hill commons for rent (typically, a shilling an acre for rye and half that for oats) but only on a temporary basis. Plots would usually be cultivated only once every five or ten years with the length of the fallow gap depending on how long it took to restore fertility. Small enclosures and even old plough furrows can still be seen on aerial photographs of the open upland areas.

By the seventeenth century, such shifting cultivation was sometimes followed by squatter settlements, often little more than hovels, edging up the combes and tucked into roadside verges. Quarter Session records suggest that rural 'squatting' ran on into the nineteenth century with continued occupation being allowed by the courts only in cases of extreme hardship. Not a few of today's smart 'second homes' have their origins in such poverty.

Woodland

Much of the hill area, especially on the eastern slopes of the Quantocks was well wooded with substantial areas of common woodland aside from that reserved for manorial estate owners. Commoners were allowed specific rights to take some small amounts of wood but, unsurprisingly, such rights were often exceeded with miscreants brought to court (and thus into the historical record). In 1640 a tenant at Over Stowey felled and sold thirteen acres of wood without permission, growing corn on the land. Another typical case was brought by the Stogursey agent of the Earl of Northumberland against one William Mullins of Bagborough who is 'building of a house in the highway and he hath stolen from my lord's wood three score and fourteen oaken rafters and lastes and three or four alders'.[19]

Wood was valuable not just for construction. Bark was increasingly valuable for leather tanning with the sale of bark from the 500 oaks felled to build Crowcombe Court from woodland on the estate yielding a rich return. Scrub woodland was also widely used for charcoal burning with the burners leading a strange, isolated life living alongside their fickle, ever-demanding kilns. The Quantock landmark of Walford's Gibbet records the history of a man who, like his father, was a charcoal burner.

At the other end of the social scale from the great estates, the commons provided a rare if uncertain source of income for the very poorest in rural society. The scrubby areas on the hills provided three further resources: furze collected for kindling, materials for broom making, and finally whortleberries. Berta Lawrence in her *Somerset Journal* recalls her meeting with an eighty-year old man in Five Lords Combe, the last of the Quantock broom makers.[20] Collecting 'worts' in autumn provided income for landless labourers to pay their rent or buy clothes.

Clothmaking

Agriculture was the leading occupation over the early modern period. But even in as rural an area as the Quantocks, there were some employed in industry. As we noted in Chapter 4, clothmaking was the vital industry in the region at the end of the Middle Ages and was to continue to be important for another 150 years.[21] Bench-ends from this period celebrate both the craftsmen who made clothmaking possible and the ships who carried wool in and local cloth out (Fig. 5.11). The water bailiff accounts and port books for Bridgwater throw light on the cloth trade: imported Brazil wood (which gave a red dye) and alum (a mordant or dye fixer) was being stored for 'Crydell of Stowie' in 1597 while woad (a blue dye) was bound for Thomas Strange of Stogursey. Export records include the small 8-ton *Speedwell* of Stogursey found carrying apples across to the channel to Tenby in October 1603 and calfskins and tanned leather to Swansea three months later.[22]

Fig. 5.11 The clothmaking industry began in the medieval period but reached its peak after the reformation. (Left) Evidence of early stages in the industry are given in the depiction of a fuller with his tools in a famous Spaxton church benchend. (Right) Exports of cloth, mainly through the ports of Bridgwater and Watchet, were by the kind of coastal vessel shown on this Bishops Lydeard church bench-end.

With later technological improvements the comparative advantages (small clear streams and water power) of the hill foot villages waned and by the time of the eighteenth century descriptions, the industry is dominantly an urban occupation. In the period 1640 to 1714 studied by Ashford, the woollen industry went through a number of changes.[23] Taunton began to concentrate on a different type of cloth (serge), and major centres were developed at Monksilver and Stogumber in the west of the region and Fiddington, Holford, and East Quantoxhead in the east. Welsh and Irish wool continued to be imported into local ports to supplement Exmoor and Quantock wool. Exports continued from Minehead, Watchet and Bridgwater but by this period cloth was reaching both the West Indies and the new colonies in New England and Pennsylvania by vessels such as the *Samuel and Mary* and the *Willing Mind*. Some cloth was sent to Bristol and Exeter for finishing and onward export by larger vessels.

Locally, Sir George Luttrell gave Dunster a yarn market in 1586 and by the middle of the following century it was drawing cloth merchants from as far as Stogursey. Tucking and fulling mills continued to operate across the Quantock region with records between 1647 and 1752 including locations at Dodington, Kilve, Kingston St Mary, Nether Stowey, Old Cleeve, Over Stowey, Spaxton, Stogumber, Stogursey, Stringston, Tolland and Watchet. In terms of records of operatives the three leading centres of the industry continued to be, as in the late medieval period, Watchet, Stogumber and Stogursey. Women were involved in the woollen industry at several stages, even including coastal shipping, but their main role was as spinners. In 1616 Joan Lawrence of Fiddington died possessing sheep, wool and a pair of looms while in 1690 Agnes Pollard of nearby Holford left serge cloth. But by the end of the century there are records of poverty, even starvation among the woollen workers and the local village industries appeared to be in decline.

The transport economy

For most of the early modern period the problems that beset late medieval transport remained. Away from coastal harbours or navigable rivers, road transport was slow, difficult and expensive. Estimates for the relative costs of hauling bulky goods (e.g. building stone) overland or by water suggest a cost ratio as high as 10:1 in medieval England and there are few indications of improvement in the two following centuries.[24] Most personal travel was by foot over shorter distances, by horseback for longer journeys: carriage transport was rare. When heavy loads could no longer be carried by water, they were split up into smaller weights to be moved by horse or mule trains moving in single file. Still heavier loads were moved locally by broad-wheeled waggons or sledges. Ways of reducing weight and bulk were typified by charcoal-burning: this turned a bulky and low-value product (wood) into a compact and valuable one (charcoal). Only the best stone (e.g. the golden-coloured Ham stone from the quarries near Martock in south Somerset) used for detailed carving and window mouldings was moved longer distances and then in a semi-finished state: otherwise coarser local stone had to serve. Finished cloth was more economical to move than the bulky wool. Livestock which could walk to market was an exception: flocks of sheep and herds of cattle and horses were driven along old routes such as the Quantock ridgeways (see the map of Saxon routes in Fig. 1.6). Such routes became in effect 'green roads' where animals could be rested for the night. Although local markets at Bridgwater and Taunton or the port of Watchet were the main destinations, Somerset records refer to cattle being driven as far as Winchester and even London.

One reason for the poor state of roads lay mainly in the fragmented responsibility for their upkeep. An Act of Parliament in 1555 placed the burden of maintenance was placed on the parish, which had to elect two 'way wardens' annually. These in turn obliged householders of the parish to give a period of 'statutory' labour (originally four days but later increased) to repair the roads with farmers in the parish obliged to provide horses and carts to assist. Despite these laws the roads got worse and complaints to Justices of the Peace increased.

One solution to the problem first proposed in 1663 was to form a Turnpike Trust.[25] A turnpike was a road on which a toll was collected at a toll-gate. Hundreds of such trusts were formed by Acts of Parliament to allow local people, to raise money by public loans to build new roads or repair existing ones. Users were charged a fee based on the size of the wagon or carriage, the number of horses pulling it, or the number and type of animals in the drove or flock. Foot travellers were exempt from tolls, as were soldiers, and coaches carrying Royal Mail.

The first trust in Somerset was set up at Bath in 1707-8 with Bristol following in 1731. Over the rest of the century almost every town in the county followed. The Quantocks were directly affected by three trusts: the Bridgwater Trust (created in 1730), the Taunton Trust (1752) and the Minehead United Trust (1765). As Fig. 5.12 shows, they spread out in a spiders-web fashion from each town progressively linking Quantock villages into their web. Such roads incorporated Thomas Telford's ideas of building road foundations with larger stones on which smaller stones were cambered to give better-draining surfaces. John Macadam improved Telford's methods while working for the Bristol Turnpike Trust and he and his sons worked on designing both the Bridgwater and Minehead tollroads.

The legacy of the turnpikes are visible in the Quantocks today. First, in the alignment of the new roads. Today's trunk roads such as the A39 and the A358 broadly follow the line of the toll roads. These replaced the village-to-village line of the local medieval roads with more direct through lines between major settlements. In hill country, gradients were lowered and curves broadened to

1 QUANTOCK LEGENDS *A dragon (the 'Gurt Wurm') that lived in Shervage Woods and ravaged the area around Holford. This late medieval bench-end from Crowcombe's church of the Holy Ghost was probably carved by Simon Warman of Bicknoller around 1534. It is one of over seventy bench ends from this period in Quantock parish churches (see map in Fig. 1.8).*

2 QUANTOCK HILLS LANDSCAPES I Two contrasting elements of uplands and valleys. *(A) View from Black Hill looking northwards down Frog Combe, a branch of the Hodder-Holford combe system. Longstone Hill (1,030 ft) forms the northern horizon. (B) Hodders Combe in the northern Quantocks, part of the largest system of branching valleys in the Quantocks (see map in Fig. 8.12).*

3 QUANTOCK HILLS LANDSCAPES II *(A) Heather moorlands near Bicknoller Post on the exposed main Quantock ridge in winter. (B) Sheep grazing in the oak woodlands on the steep combe sides at Lady's Edge. The distribution of both types of land use is shown in Fig. 8.1.*

4 BOUNDARIES *The distinctive lines of beech trees growing from a stone and clay bank is a feature familiar to all Quantock walkers. Such hedges often mark the line of old parish boundaries. This fine example from near Triscombe Stone separates Crowcombe parish (left) from Over Stowey parish (right).*

5 LITERARY AND ARTISTIC ASOCIATIONS *(A) Alfoxton House near Holford, the long-time Somerset home of the St Aubyn family, rented 1797–8 to William and Dorothy Wordsworth for the sum of £23. (B) Halsway Manor near Crowcombe, briefly a base for a school of nineteenth-century landscape painters and currently home for the English Folk Dance Society. (C) The Church House at Crowcombe was built around 1515 and stands across the road from the parish church of the Holy Ghost. It is a regular centre for exhibitions of the work of Quantock artists.*

6 GEOLOGY *(A) Folded strata of Liassic age on the Kilve foreshore. (B) Fossil Ammonite set in a wall made up of liassic limestone blocks from the local beach and located beside the path from the mill pond to the parish church of St Mary, East Quantoxhead. (C) Blue Lias blocks used for walling of farm buildings at Fairfield, Stogursey. (D) The ruined engine house of the Glebe Field copper mine near Dodington (see map in Fig. 6.3). (E) Ilfracombe Slates are widely used for walling in the southern Quantocks as here on the Halswell House estate at Goathurst.*

7 PREHISTORIC LANDSCAPES *(A) Stone cairn at Hare Knap of Bronze Age origin looking across to the Iron age camp at Dowsborough (see map in Fig. 3.4). (B) Dead Woman's Ditch, an Iron Age territorial boundary. Although the gruesome name is often linked to the Walford murder in 1789, it occurs on maps well before that date. (C) Longstone, on Longstone Hill, a boundary marker probably of Saxon age.*

8 MEDIEVAL CHURCHES *All of the thirty Quantock parish churches were in existence by early medieval times. (A) All Saints' at Aisholt clinging to its hillside now serves a small hamlet (see opening of Chapter 4). (B) St Mary's, Bishops Lydeard with its fifteenth-century tower of local sandstones dominating one of the largest villages in the region.*

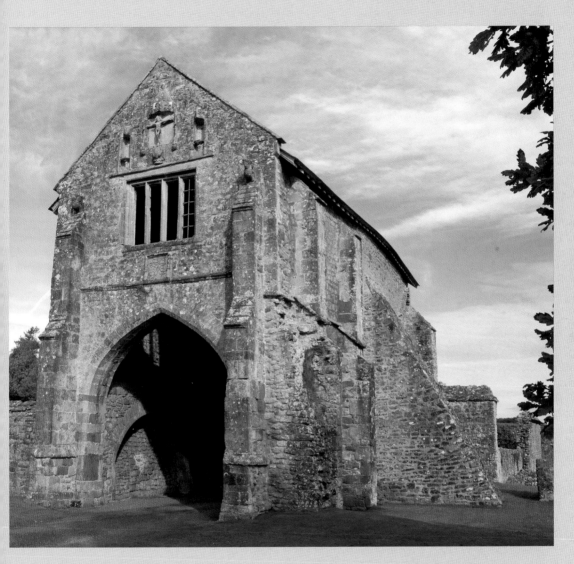

9 MONASTIC MEMORIALS *Gatehouse of Cleeve Abbey, the most complete monastic survival in Somerset (see plan in Fig. 4.9). Located in the romantically-named 'Vallis Florida', this Cistercian Abbey was founded in 1186 and dissolved by Henry VIII in 1537. The gatehouse dates from the thirteenth century but was remodelled three centuries later when a Latin inscription 'gate be open, shut to no honest man' was added above the arch.*

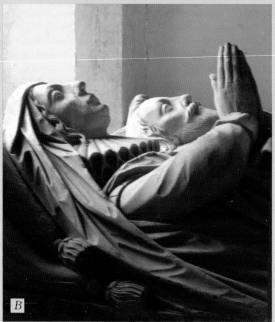

10 A QUANTOCK FAMILY CHAPEL *Several churches in the area have chapels dedicated to the local lords of the manor. (A) The superb seventeenth-century Tynte family memorial in the parish church of St Edward, King and Martyr, at Goathurst, with grieving children kneeling in remembrance. (B) Detail showing Sir Nicholas Halswell (died 1633) and his wife who predeceased him in 1627. (C) Eldest son (of six sons) and eldest daughter (of three) shown meeting at the south-east corner of the monument.*

11 COUNTRY HOUSES *The region is rich in small country houses. (A) Nettlecombe Court (with the adjacent parish church of St Mary the Virgin) is largely a late-Elizabethan mansion, extensively rebuilt in 1878. It is currently the Leonard Wills Field Studies centre. (B) Barford Park, Enmore, was built in 1710 for the Jeanes family with a third storey and flanking wings added later in the century.*

12 FOLLIES *Landscaping ideas in the eighteenth century made extensive use of follies as visual markers. (A) The Temple of Harmony is one of several structures in the grounds of Halswell House, Goathurst. It dates from 1767 and is based on the first-century Temple of Fortuna Virilis in Rome. (B) Willett Tower is somewhat later (circa 1820). It crowns a wooded hill in the Brendons where it can be seen for many miles around as a marker for the western part of the region.*

13 QUANTOCK COAST *The northern coast is an odd mixture of remote beauty and over-development (see also Plate 15A). (A) Remains today of the harbour at Lilstock built by the Sir John Acland around 1820 to serve the Fairfield Estate. (B) West jetty at Watchet, the Quantock's main harbour. (C) Combwich pill on the River Parrett. (D) A military base at Doniford, converted after World War II to a holiday village.*

14 VICTORIAN BUILDINGS *(A) One of the most dramatic examples was the complete rebuilding by the Acland-Hood family of the the parish church dedicated to St Etheldreda at West Quantoxhead to the design of John Norton. (B) The 1857 Tudor-style gate house near Plainsfield designed by Henry Clutton for Lord Taunton's great Quantock estate at Over Stowey. (C) Watchet Methodist chapel, c1871. (D) Williton Union Poor House, c1840. (E) Tone Vale Mental Hospital in Bishops Lydeard parish, c1897.*

15 POWER SOURCES *(A) The largest building investment in Quantock history began in 1957 with the construction of a nuclear power station at Hinkley Point on the coast north of Stogursey. Looking south from the seaward side shows A on the left and B on the right. (B) Such developments contrasts with the local use of water power as at Holford tannery (see map in Fig. 6.4). (C) The monument 'Ebb and Flow' on the bank of the River Parrett commemorates both the traditional small-scale use of tidal power and its large-scale potential for the future (see map in Fig. 8.10).*

16 QUANTOCK MISCELLANY (A) Replanting of the old dying beech clump (right) with new trees (left) on Cothelstone Beacon at the southern end of the Hills. (B) Hardwood trees planted on the edge of the Great Wood plantation by the Forestry Commission. (C) Start of the West Somerset Coast Path at Steart. (D) Bicknoller Post on the main north-south Quantock ridge walk. (E) Illegal dumping is an occasional problem: a burnt-out car being removed from below Beacon Hill. (F) Great Wood Camp established by the Scripture Union in 1946 at Adscombe, Over Stowey.

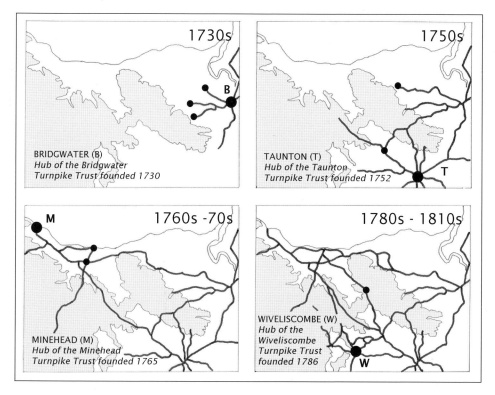

Fig. 5.12 Extension of turnpike roads into the Quantocks in the eighteenth century. The four maps show the progressive growth of roads based on the surrounding hubs of Bridgwater (from 1730), Taunton (from 1752), Minehead (from 1765) and Wiveliscombe (from 1785). Source: *Drawn from data in Bentley & Murless, 1985 (note 24).*

allow easier movement of wagons and carriages. A second legacy is in the scores of tollhouses which survive today, usually at the present roadside and with walls angled in a half-hexagonal form to allow keepers good view of the road in each direction. The late eighteenth-century stone tollhouse in St Mary's Street, Nether Stowey, built by the Minehead trust at its junction with the Bridgwater trust is one good example (Fig. 5.13). Williton has two other fine examples at Tower Hill and on the Bridgwater Road. In the Brendons, a turnpike house survives as Elworthy Cross House while a road which skirted the village (and thus saved the toll) was dubbed 'Save Penny Lane'.

Many of the region's turnpike roads had distinctive milestones planted along the highway verge. Although many were removed at the time of invasion fears early in World War II, a few fine examples survive. The restored milestone outside Cothelstone Manor on the Bridgwater to Bishops Lydeard turnpike and inscribed '8 miles to Bridgwater' is of granite and cast iron made by a Bristol foundry (Fig. 5.13). East of the Nether Stowey tollhouse and set in the vicarage wall is another milestone which reads: 'Here Ends Bridgewater Road'.

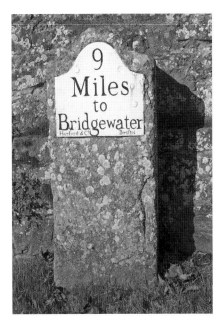 

Fig. 5.13 Relicts of the turnpike age. (Left) *Restored milestone marker at Cothelstone erected by the Bridgwater Turnpike Trust on their route across the southern Quantocks to Bishops Lydeard.* (Right) *The stone toll house built by the Minehead Turnpike Trust at the eastern end of one of their toll roads at Nether Stowey.*

At first the toll roads served their purpose. They allowed the development of a system of cross-country mails and coach routes using the turnpike routes. Taverns which offering changes of horses flourished. A good example occurs at the main crossroads in the centre of the small town of Williton. This was the location of an inn called, appropriately, the 'Coach and Horses' in 1742; rebuilt to accommodate increasing turnpike traffic, it was renamed the 'Wyndham' (after the local landowning family) in 1830 and changed to 'Egremont' in 1861 after Sir Charles' enoblement.

With the coming of the railways from 1841 (Fig. 6.5), high-value turnpike traffic was undercut and the trusts began to make severe losses. Between 1867 and 1883 all the Somerset trusts were dissolved. They had served a useful purpose but under the Local Government Act of 1888 the care of such roads passed to the newly-formed Somerset County Council.

POPULATION GROWTH

At the start of the early modern period Henry VIII's chancellor, Thomas Cromwell, ordered each parish in England and Wales to keep a register of baptisms, marriages and deaths. At first lists were kept on loose sheets, many of which have been lost or destroyed, but in 1597 a new order required each parish should keep its records in a bound register and that earlier records should be transcribed into it. For the Quantocks we have records surviving for all parishes: the earliest is Cannington (from 1559) and the latest, Broomfield (1630).[26]

Although long neglected by demographers, work by Sauvy in France on commune registers showed the huge potential of such local parish records for making estimates of past population movement. At Cambridge, the historical geographer, E. A. Wrigley, set up a research group (CAMPOP) to make use of English parish records. Through an ingenious but very laborious method called 'back projection' Wrigley and his colleagues were able to reconstruct the basic demography of England from 1541 through to 1871.[27] Because of the detailed work involved, not all five thousand English parishes could be covered but a representative sample of 404 parishes distributed widely across the country were selected for transcription and study. Ten parishes in Wrigley's sample were drawn from Somerset and although no Quantock parish was included, two (Bridgwater and North Petherton) were located on its very edge.

Two results of Wrigley's work which throw some light on the Quantocks situation are shown in Fig. 5.14. First, growth was shown to see-saw over the period. We can recognize three phases: a period up to the 1630s marked by fluctuating growth; a follow-up period of stagnation and decline up to the 1720s; and fluctuating and then sustained high growth for the rest of the eighteenth century. The general picture is of growth interrupted by setbacks: the 1560s, the 1660s–1680s, and the 1730s were all decades of decline. Whether this was due poor harvests, political uncertainty, epidemic diseases, the collapse of local industry, or overseas migration remains to be teased out.

Second, an overall estimate of England's total population every five years is given from 1541. This shows a more than threefold increase over the 270-year period from 2.8 to 8.7 million. If we take the known census value for 1801

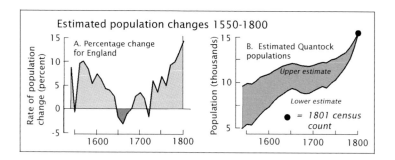

Fig. 5.14 Graph of estimated population change in the Early Modern period using Wrigley's back-projection methods. (Left) Percentage change in the population of England, 1541–1801. Note the sharp decline in growth in the 1650s. (Right) Estimated change in the Quantock population. See discussion in text. Source: Wrigley & Schofield, 1989 (note 26), 208-9.

when the Quantock population stood at 15,520 (see the discussion at the end of Chapter 6), then we can use this as an anchor point. Applying the back-projection curve shows that, if the Quantocks had behaved demographically like the rest of England, they would have had a 1541 population of just 4,960.

But that estimate looks too low. It would imply nil growth over the whole of the medieval period if our Domesday survey total of around 5,000 (given in Chapter 4) is correct. Since our region was a part of England outside the 'boom' areas (around London and in the industrializing Midlands and North) it is likely to have grown more slowly than England as a whole. Since we don't know how much lower, the upper curve in Fig. 5.14 (right) sketches in the course which would have been followed if the Quantocks had grown at only half the national rate. The shaded area between the two lines shows the zone within which the trajectory of Quantock growth probably lay. This would give a figure of up to 9,800 in 1550 and of 12,600 in 1750. This is much more plausible and fits in with other Somerset estimates such as Edmund's Rack's survey (accompanying the Revd John Collinson's *History of Somersetshire*).[28]

Six

LATE GEORGIAN AND
VICTORIAN LANDSCAPES

> The time is not far off when we shall be able to take our coffee and
> write while going noiselessly and smoothly at 45 miles per hour.
>   Isambard Kingdom Brunel
> (writing in his diary on his first journey by train, 5 December 1831).[1]

Only a few months before his death, Brunel signed off the survey of a new line
through the Crowcombe corridor linking his Bristol and Exeter railway at
Taunton with the tidewater port of Watchet. On 7th April 1859 Lady Isabel
Acland Hood, whose father's enthusiastic backing had secured the line, turned
the first sod on the West Somerset Railway. The location was at Crowcombe
Heathfield, half way between the junction at Norton Fitzwarren near Taunton
on the Bristol-Exeter line and its terminus at Watchet. With the construction
of this fifteen-mile line (it was later extended to Minehead), the Quantock
region was firmly connected into the powerful Victorian grid that was trans-
forming England as it was so much of the rest of the world.

The visitor to Crowcombe Heathfield station today can pick up something
of the spirit of this railway revolution. The railway lines the platform, the
signal box, the waiting room, the occasional steam engine, all speak to a
bygone and confident age. Of course not all is what it seems. Twin tracks of
standard gauge have replaced Brunel's single broad-gauge line. Much was
swept away when the line closed to goods in 1964 and to passengers in 1971.
Since the reopening of the line as far as Bishops Lydeard in June 1979, hard
work and voluntary help have transformed the scene of abandonment. The
fact that the original signal box (destroyed by fire) was replaced by one from
Ebbw Vale or that a goods-office hut hails from Flax Bourton or the distinctive lamp posts from Tiverton Junction adds to its charm.[2] The sense of
Victorian heritage is undimmed.

In this chapter we review the revolutionary era that stretches from the middle of the eighteenth century through to the end of the next: a period we dub 'late Georgian and Victorian' to roughly encompass the reigns of five monarchs and one regent. First, we review the rise and decline of Quantock farming that, at least in the period of 'high farming' underpinned the region's wealth and the industries that grew from it. Second, we turn to the transport revolution that radically altered the spatial relations between one part of the region and another. In a third section we turn to the legacy of building, both private and public, ecclesiastical and secular, by which the Georgians and Victorians changed the Quantock built landscape. While few parish churches escaped Victorian 'improvement' the number of wholly new structures was sparser. Finally we sum up the changes by looking at what happened to Quantock population over the period. Why did the numbers recorded rise to a peak at mid-century to (a peak the Quantocks were not to match again for another century) and then decline? In each section we try to interpret historical trends, pin these to specific locations, and hunt for their legacy today.

ECONOMIC CYCLES IN THE QUANTOCKS

Although agriculture was the bedrock of Quantock wealth throughout the period and its largest employer, the sector went through a major long-term cycle: climbing slowly to a peak in the 1850s and then starting a decline which was to last until the Great War. Similar though shorter economic cycles afflicted mining and manufacturing. We look at each in turn.

The long-term cycle in Quantock farming

The founding of the Bath and West Society in 1777 was a signal of the trend towards modernization in Quantock farming.[3] In the same decade Arthur Young visited the area as part of his tours of rural England. He noted with approval that three to five year crop rotations were common on the better land around Bishops Lydeard. He was followed in 1778, by Shaw who describes the vale of Taunton Deane as 'beautiful with green meadows and delightful with orchards'. John Billingsley's *General View of the Agriculture of the County of Somerset* (1795) describes the Bishops Lydeard area (Grade I in Fig. 2.12) as a 'land of Canaan' where climate and soils were better, arable and pasture was well balanced, and agricultural methods more progressive. Here the 'new husbandry' was becoming well established:

> In the parish of Bishops-Lidiard they frequently plough their wheat stubble soon after harvest, giving it a good dressing of rotten dung, and let it lie in ridges during the winter. In the months of February and March they sow

carrots, which are fit to be dug up the latter end of July: they then sow turnips or plant cabbages, and after these sow barley and grass feeds. On rich sandy loam, this husbandry cannot be too much extolled.[4]

But all Quantock was not Canaan. On the poorer land around the hills, the harvest was a month later and yields were lighter. The loose shelly rock and damp climate made wheat ripening hazardous and oats were more widely grown on the farms flanking the hills. As today, the upland was uncultivated but supported numbers of sheep and young cattle which in autumn were sold at the local fairs (then Bishops Lydeard, Bridgwater, Broomfield, North Petherton, Taunton and West Bagborough). Many sheep were kept on local lowland farms for the winter and pastured on the hills in summer. Billingsley notes the value of the earth banks topped with beech trees on the hills serving as boundary, windbreak, and source of fuel. But the many coppices which flanked the hills were largely of scrub oak and under no system of management.

Agricultural improvement came in two ways: intensifying farming on old land and the extending farming into new lands. The problem in the Quantocks was that most land which was worth farming had already been enclosed and there were few new frontiers to explore. So although Somerset recorded 173 Parliamentary Enclosure Awards in the century and a half after 1720 only seven of these related to the Quantock parishes: Crowcombe (1776), Durleigh (1802), Cannington with Stogursey and Stockland Bristol (1803), West Bagborough (1810), Lilstock (1811), Elworthy (1831), and Cannington and Otterhampton (1867).[5] The enclosure process is illustrated in Fig. 6.1 by the Crowcombe award.[6] This took in 'waste' land both on the steep western slopes the Quantock hills, and on the pebble beds of the Vale of Stogumber. New land was divided between four people with the lords of the two Crowcombe manors taking over nine tenths. The map shows what happened to the land between the date of the enclosure and the Tithe map record of 1842. Enclosure on the Devonian beds of the high Quantocks had little effect on the previous land use pattern but on the lighter soils of Heddon and Crowcombe Heathfield enclosure brought improvement.

We are fortunate in having a good description of Quantock farming at its peak from Thomas Acland in his Royal Agricultural Society report on *The Farming of Somersetshire* (1851).[7] He farmed at Tetton in Kingston St Mary parish so had a good local knowledge. Like Billingsley before him, Acland is careful to distinguish between the three grades of Quantock land. Large farms on the Class I land around Bishops Lydeard gain his highest praise. Mechanization was increasing with threshing machines (a few driven by water-power from the swift Quantock streams) a recent innovation. Artificial fertilizers were in use and field drainage using clay pipes from Bridgwater tile makers

Fig. 6.1 Late eighteenth-century enclosures. (Above) *View north of hill land enclosed in Crowcombe parish after 1780.* (Below) *Three areas within the parish enclosed under the 1780 Crowcombe enclosure award. Comparison with the Crowcombe tithe map of 1842 shows relatively little change in land use on the Quantock Hills but extensive afforestation and arable farming on the other two enclosed lowland areas.* Source: *Haggett, 1953 (note 4), 61.*

allowed better yields on clay soils. Size of fields was increasing 'in the interests of efficient farming' but hampered by the massive traditional Quantock hedge-bank and the intricate intermingling of field ownership. Owner-labour relations were also changing and Acland met one farmer who paid wages wholly in money: a 'revolutionary' change from the usual part-money part-cider payment. Cider production itself was changing with orchards around his own village growing 'Kingston Blacks' which yielded a high quality sweet cider in contrast to the rough cider characteristic of the rest of the region.

In contrast to the rich south-west margin, production in the Quantock Hills on Class III land (Fig. 2.14) continued to be marginal though better than the Brendons or Exmoor. He thought this due to the large number of 'gentlemens' residences' which flanked the lower slopes of the hills. On the intermediate

(Class II) land the five-year rotation system of wheat, turnips, barley and two years grass shows the successful adaptation of regimes to poorer soils and damper climate. Root crops were now an established part of the rotation cycle and Acland comments on use of children in the area for the weeding and thinning demanded by the new crops. Sheep were still of considerable importance in the farm economy and after fattening in winter on corn they were sold at the spring fairs for good prices. Of the southern Quantocks, he comments that despite the intricate nature of the country and the steep combes 'there is farming here of which for neatness and practical efficiency the men of the Eastern counties would not be ashamed'. But the honeymoon was not to last.

Decline and fall in farming

Rapid decline of agriculture in the second half of the nineteenth century is shown most clearly in the fall of population in the rural parishes (discussed at the end of this chapter). From 1873, annual farm statistics across England were collected by the Board of Agriculture on a parish by parish basis.[8] From the records of the fourteen central Quantock parishes with land running up onto the main hill ridge, we can reconstruct the startling changes. By the end of the century, crop land had fallen by a quarter, the sharpest fall in wheat where the acreage dropped by 45 per cent: in 1873 one field in six was under wheat, a quarter-century later it was one field in fourteen. Fields abandoned for grain crops had been turned over to permanent pasture (both for mowing and for grazing) which had increased from 40 to 55 percent of farm acreage. Since overall farm acreage had remained roughly constant over the same period, the fall in cropland had been made up by a shift to permanent pasture (both for mowing and for grazing). At the start of the period pasture had accounted for 40 percent of Quantock farm acreage, by the end 55 percent. An illustration of the change in cropland in a single Quantock parish (Kilve) is shown over a longer time period in Fig. 6.2.[9]

The Quantock parishes reflect the dilemma of British agriculture in this period. Price levels of home-produced cereals crashed as they were undercut by cheaper imports, largely from Canada and Australia. In consequence, livestock prices were relatively higher than cereal prices, and it was more profitable for a Quantock farmer to market his cereal crops as livestock or livestock products rather than grain. The demand for farm labour followed the trend down and, as we see in our later discussion of population, all the more remote Quantock parishes showed a sharply falling population.

Mining booms and busts

While the wealth of the Quantocks continued to rest on its agriculture, other sources came occasionally into play. If we exclude the Brendon iron-ore fields

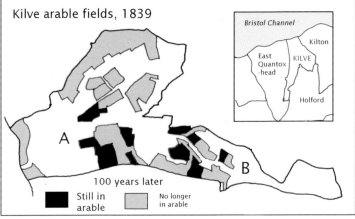

Fig. 6.2 Declining arable land in the coastal belt. (Above) View east across the coastal lowland of Kilve parish. (Below) Distribution of arable fields on the 1839 Tithe Map and Apportionment for Kilve (1839). A hundred years later (in the Land Utilization Survey of 1931/32) only those fields shown in black were still in arable use: the rest had changed to pasture (in the lowlands) or reverted to rough grazing (in the hills). Source: Haggett, 1953 (note 5), 64, 74.

(they lie just to the west of our region) then the most significant mining in the Quantocks was for copper.[10] As we noted in Chapter 2, this outcrops in veins at a number of points around the Quantocks. Most attempts to win copper (such as at Bincombe, 1690-1724) were speculative ventures which resulted in little ore product and can be dismissed as 'the brain children of rogues if not scoundrels'. Promoters exploited wealthy but inexperienced landowners, with the Bishop of Winchester as one notable victim.

One exception to this 'hobby mining' was at Dodington on the eastern slopes of the hills. Here the land belonged to Richard Greville (later Duke of Buckingham and Chandos) and was crossed by a promising band of copper ore (see Fig.2.10) which zig-zagged across the parish. Here substantial mining activity occurred in two phases. In the first, 1785 to 1801, mining was largely financed by the Buckingham family. Trial pits were dug and lateral adits driven to follow promising veins of copper. A plant for crushing and sorting the ore was built at Newhall, and its output taken by horse and cart to the little river port at Combwich for export to Bristol for final smelting. The labour employed in mining came mainly from Cornwall with some Derbyshire miners and a few colliers from north Somerset brought in to help with engineering works. Numbers were never large, a core of twenty Cornish miners with three experienced 'captains' to oversee below and above ground work. Women and children employed at Newhall in ore sorting swelled the numbers.

As often with mining, water proved the great problem particularly as adits were driven down towards the levels where the best ore was predicted to be found. Output was never profitable enough to justify building the steam engines used to drain Cornish mines and so water control had to rest on gravity-draining through cleverly graded adits. Worsening mining conditions as the digging got deeper and falling prices for the mined ore combined to bring the project to an end in 1801. The boom had lasted just 26 years.

There matters might have stood but for the intervention of the remarkable Tom Poole of Nether Stowey (who we have already met befriending Coleridge in Chapter 1). Rising copper price tempted Poole to re-examine the Dodington prospect and to re-open the mine in 1817. To do this he needed a consortium of investors which included the Quaker industrialist Thomas Fox of Wellingon and members of the Lutrell family at Dunster. Josiah Wedgewood was also approached by Poole but proved 'totally averse' to investing. Wedgewood's instincts were right: the second phase of mining lasted only four years finally closing in 1821. Despite a spasm of interest when gold was found at South Molton on Exmoor in 1840 and a brief interest in mining at Broomfield when a Broomfield Consols Copper and Silver Lead Mining Company was formed in 1854, Quantock mining activity had ceased.

Activity must have been at its peak when Dorothy Wordsworth records in her diary for March 23rd 1798 that she had walked with her brother and Coleridge (see Chapter 1) to the 'Miners House' (probably the mine Counting House at which miners collected their pay). It's likely that her brother, William also went down into one of the shafts for next year in Germany he refused to go down the Clausthal mine on the grounds there was nothing new to see there.[11] As Fig. 6.3 shows, there are remnants of the industry in today's landscape. The remains of the Glebe Field engine house, even without its original tall chimney, is evocative of the Cornish landscape as are the remains of the drying sheds nearby. A less tangible reminder comes from the boost to local Methodism.

Three other minerals were used throughout the region: clays, limestones and buiding stone. Clays were confined to a few coastal and riverine areas. Brickfields were developed at Combwich and the output exported via the

Fig. 6.3   Relicts from the brief copper-mining boom around Dodington give the landscape a Cornish look. Remains of the Glebe engine house. For a map of the workings see Fig. 2.10.

Parrett. Blue Anchor also had a brick kiln.[12] Limestones, widely distributed throughout the area, were locally quarried and burnt to provide lime for agricultural and building use. Along the northern coast, lime kilns are abundant as at Kilve Beach, at Doniford, and at Warren Farm west of Watchet (see Fig. 2.11) with both coal and limestone brought in from South Wales. The latter were used from 1850s for the production of hydraulic and Portland cement and for Plaster of Paris using limestone and gypsum quarried from the nearby cliffs. There is also an unusually complete lime kiln at Ash Priors which burnt limestone from the lower sandstone conglomerates.

The third mineral in common use was building stone. The Quantock regions is peppered with small, shallow quarries. High transport costs meant that stone could not be moved far overland and most houses that could afford to use stone in construction used very local quarries on the estate. Examples of the use of building stone in walling were given in Plates 6C and 6E. An example of the use of local stone is provided by Quantock Lodge at Over Stowey which was built in the 1850s from a local volcanic rock (Schalstein) from nearby Bin Combe (Plate 14B). Large-scale quarrying as at Triscombe on the western edge of the Quantocks, is largely a twentieth-century phenomenon.

Manufacturing and mill power

Although the Quantocks were never a major industrial area, a small scatter of manufacturing sites were developed over the period. Many were associated with the growth of Watchet as its largest settlement and a convenient import-export point. Paper making was established in Watchet from 1750 with the

Wansborough paper mill. It remains today athough most of the original buildings have been replaced and its iconic detached chimney is scheduled for demolition. Steam-powered flour milling flourished there from the 1830s using both local and imported grain and imported coal. Grinding stones were replaced by roller milling in 1885 but after a major fire in 1911 the company was relocated to Bristol.

Outside Watchet, the tanning industry was important in three Quantock locations: Nether Stowey, Holford and Old Cleeve. The most important centre for tanning was at Nether Stowey where the industry brought fortune to the Poole family from the early eighteenth century. It was located in a complex of buildings behind their fine family home in Castle Street. It was the profits from the tannery industry that allowed Thomas Poole to find Coleridge a cottage in Lime Street in 1797 and to support a literary circle that included the Wordsworths, Charles Lamb, Robert Southey and Sir Humphrey Davey. But his contributions to village life were much wider: in 1807 he founded a women's friendly society (whose procession to the church continues each year) and in 1812 built a schoolroom.

The complex of tannery buildings at Holford were developed by James Hayman around 1840 (Fig. 6.4). The most distinctive feature today is the large 25 feet overshot wheel with associated gearing which is still in place. Cast by the Bridgwater ironfounders, Culverwell, it was assembled in 1892 by Charles Sellick of Fiddington. The tannery was closed in 1900 and the buildings (including the water wheel) now form the Combe House Hotel. A third tannery at Old Cleeve was established in 1876 by John Wood.

Silk manufacturing was an important but short-lived enterprise at both Holford and Over Stowey.[13] The silk factory near Holford was converted from an old woollen mill at the start of the nineteenth century. Some small buildings survive as ruins but the outline of a larger factory can be traced, as can three wheel-pits using water-power from the Holford streams. Aley Road at Marsh Mills near Over Stowey was the location of a second silk factory at the beginning of the nineteenth century. By 1843, evidence given to a Select Committee by its owner suggests it employed 'several hundreds of the female children and adults'. The leat remains as evidence of water power, a feature described by the Revd. Holland in his diary for 15th July 1816 as the 'new canal'.

Minor industries were scattered across local farms. In the Victorian period most produced limited amounts of their own cider, often used as part-payment for farm workers in lieu of wages. But a few breweries in the area were commercial enterprises on a far larger scale. The Stogumber Brewery was established south of the village by George Elers shortly before 1840 using water from local springs and wells. Its Medicinal Pale Ale, using water from nearby Harry Hill's well, earned a widespread reputation. But competition from larger companies

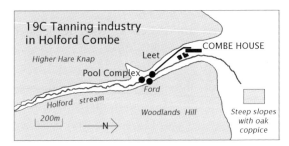

Fig. 6.4 Although the wooded combes around the Quantocks are thought of today as rustic backwaters, some were once centres of industry using oak bark from the oak woodlands as raw material for tanning. (Above left) *Map of Holford Combe showing the tannery complex developed by James Hayman from 1840.* (Above right) *A giant water wheel (25ft) cast by Culverwell of Bridgwater and assembled in 1892 provided power for the tannery. It was driven by water from the main Holford stream using leats and an overshoot system.* (Below) *The main tannery buildings are now a pleasant country hotel.* Lower photo courtesy of Combe House Hotel.

(such as Bridgwater's Starkey, Knight and Ford) weeded out such small-scale competition and brewing ceased in 1910.

Manufacturing needed power but unlike the growing industrial areas of England in the Midlands and North, there were no local coalfields in west Somerset. There was the occasional futile project to discover local coal sources (such as the sinking of a coal mine near Crowcombe in 1753) but coal needed to be imported with South Wales as the dominant source.[14] It was brought not only into the small ports of Watchet, Lilstock and Combwich (and, of course, Bridgwater) but landed at high tide on the beach at places like Blue Anchor and Shurton. Landowning families with coastal estates made their own arrangements and in 1855 at West Quantoxhead, coking coal was brought into the private wharf to power a small private plant built in 1855 to light St. Audries House. Although now a dwelling house, the building has retained its distinctive chimney and character. As the decades went on, the spread of the railways widened and cheapened access to imported coal stocks but distribution away from the harbours or railheads remained expensive. Heather Riley's research has shown that the Quantock woodlands were more heavily used for charcoal production than hitherto realized, this light and readily-shipped product being widely used for domestic heating.[15]

Given fuel scarcity, local water power remained of key importance in generating local industry. Water wheels varied greatly in size and power. One of the largest in the area and indeed the whole county has survived at Volis Farm, near Kingston St Mary where the 32-ft wheel was cast at North Looe, Cornwall, and installed in 1847. At the other extreme, a 4-ft spit-turning wheel has survived in the kitchen on Dodington Hall to remind us of domestic use. A more common size is typified by the 16-ft wheels at Orchard Mill and Bridge Mill, Williton, the first overshot and the second undershot. Wheels of this kind could be manufactured locally and that at Bridge Farm was installed in 1890 by the millwright, John Chidgey of Watchet, at a cost of £75 5s 11d. While such wheels were usually confined to corn milling, estates such as Orchard Wyndham also used them for saw milling.

THE TRANSPORT REVOLUTION

The middle part of the nineteenth century was dominated by railway building. Three lines affected the Quantock region: the main Bristol-Exeter line, the offshoot branch of the West Somerset Railway, and the mineral line built from the Brendon iron mines to Watchet.[16] We look at each before considering harbours and canals.

Trunk and branch lines

The first main railway through Somerset only grazes our region but was critical in its development, not least in its impact on Bridgwater and Taunton. It remains the dominant rail route today. The Bristol and Exeter Railway Act was approved by Parliament in 1836 and construction began shortly thereafter. As Fig. 6.4 shows, the line swept south around the Quantocks reaching Bridgwater by 1841, Taunton by 1842, and (after tunnelling delays on the Devonshire border) Exeter by 1844. Brilliantly planned by its chief engineer, Brunel, to maximize traffic and minimize construction hazards (such as the peat lands of the Somerset levels) it was an engineering and commercial success.

The achievements of the new system brought demands for branch-line connections spreading out from this main artery. The arrival of the Bristol and Exeter trunk line at Bridgwater set off a flurry of interest in an east-west line north of the Quantocks to link to Watchet and tap the un-served coastal areas to the west. In the decade after 1845 three schemes were proposed ranging from an ambitious schemes for a 'Somersetshire and North Devon Railway' termi-

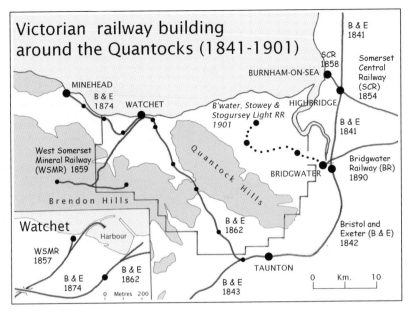

Fig. 6.5 Railway building in the Quantocks. Map of railway lines in and around the Quantock region. They range in age from the first extension of the Bristol and Exeter line in 1841 to the planned (but not built) Bridgwater, Stowey and Stogursey Light Railway proposed in 1901.

nating at Ilfracombe to a more modest Bridgwater-Watchet line. Not one of them was ever built for the problems of cutting and tunnelling for a coastal route north of the Quantocks proved prohibitively expensive.

In the end, when a branch line into West Somerset came it was to be Taunton and not Bridgwater that provided the anchor and the vale between the Quantocks and the Brendons that provided the route. A group of powerful West Somerset landowners (including Sir Peregrine Fuller Palmer Acland of St Audries who was to be its first chairman) met at Williton in July 1856 and put forward a plan for a broad-gauge line running northwest from Taunton to Watchet. The Act for a West Somerset Railway Company (WSR) received Royal Assent the next year and Brunel was appointed as its first engineer: it was almost his last act for he died in September 1859.

As Fig. 6.5 shows, the fifteen-mile route from Norton Fitzwarren junction to Watchet ran between the Quantocks and the Brendons along the Crowcombe corridor. The general alignment of the route was signed off by Brunel (by then a sick man and consumed with the problems of the *Great Eastern* and the Saltash bridge) but surveyed by his deputy Robert Brereton who shared his acute sensitivity to terrain. It posed some difficult problems needing both cuttings and embankments (Fig. 6.6). But despite the abnormally wet winter of 1859-60 the work was completed within three years and the line opened for traffic in March 1862, just six years after the initial Williton meeting. Despite the euphoria and the heavy backing of the Acland family, the line did not prove to be an immediate financial success and was quickly leased to the Bristol & Exeter as part of its broad gauge system.

Despite the limited success of the line to Watchet, interest in extending the railways further west persisted. Again, it was a local landowning family that took the lead when in 1871 George Fownes Luttrell from Dunster Castle put forward a plan for a Minehead Railway Company carrying the line west from Watchet for a further seven miles to Minehead. As Fig. 6.6 shows, much of the route runs through flat coastal plain and so it proved less onerous to construct than the Taunton-Watchet section. Despite financial and labour difficulties it was formally opened in July 1874. With its arrival Minehead began to develop as a late Victorian seaside resort, doubling its 1871 population (1,605) by the century end.

No sooner had it been completed than the remainder of the Bristol and Exeter empire was converted from Brunel's broad gauge to standard gauge (4ft 8 ½ inches) and by 1882 the whole of the link from Taunton to Minehead via Watchet was changed. After 26 years of independence the Minehead Railway was amalgamated with the Great Western in July 1897. The subsequent history of the West Somerset railway belongs to the next chapter but even today the line itself and the succession of small rural halts and stations provide a fascinating reminder of an heroic phase in Quantock development.

Fig. 6.6 Steam locomotive leaving Crowcombe Heathfield station and entering the deep cutting on the highest part of the line. (Lower left) Cross section of the Minehead branch with vertical exaggeration. Source: Jones, 1998 (note 16); photo by author.

The Brendon Hills-Watchet mineral railway

While the West Somerset railway was being built as an offshoot of the main Bristol-Exeter line, a railway with quite separate origins was emerging in the area.[17] Although it lies just outside our region, it proved so critical to Watchet's growth that a brief note must be included. Iron ores on the Brendon Hills had been worked on a sporadic but small-scale since Roman times but in the 1850s mining on a more extensive scale began with investment by the Ebbw Vale Company. Ore needed to be shipped to the coast for export across the Bristol Channel for smelting in South Wales. Given the location of the ore fields, the port of Watchet, was the obvious point for exports. But the design of a twelve-mile rail route linking the mines (at over 1,000 feet) and the port (at sea level) posed a considerable engineering problem. This was eventually solved by using a cable-operated mechanism to move trucks up and down a 1 in 4 incline (the Combe Row Incline) for over three quarters of a mile to the summit near Raleigh's Cross. The incline had a double set of rails with a vertical rise of over 800 feet with a winding house at the top.

Construction of the West Somerset Mineral Railway (WSMR) was begun in 1856 but, because of the steep incline, was not fully operational until 1861. Mineral traffic between the Brendon mines and the port of Watchet was heavy for the first couple of decades and there was some passenger service. But the line proved increasingly unprofitable and it was closed after forty years of operation in 1898. It reopened for a short period in 1907 but was finally abandoned in 1919. The attractive lower course of the railway can be followed today running up the valley of the Washford Brook. The WSMR terminus at Watchet can be readily traced on the ground: the stone goods shed is now a garage and the station building a set of flats. A memorial on the western pier explains how iron ore was tipped into coasters and the Exmoor National Park has plans to make the Combe Row incline accessible to the public.

Changes in water transport

While it was rail transport that transformed the Quantock connection with the rest of the country, water transport also played its part. Although the river port of Bridgwater dominated trade in central Somerset, Watchet remained a key harbour within the western Quantock region (Fig. 6.7). But it continued to be vulnerable to storms blowing up the Bristol Channel. In 1807 and again in 1838 the Wyndham family financed the rebuilding of the protective western pier (as they had in 1660 and 1797) using elm piles. Increasing use of the port for iron ore exports from the Brendon Hills and the completion of the West Somerset Mineral Railway in 1861 called for major reshaping.[18] Harbour commissioners were appointed in 1857 and James Abernethy extended the western pier (with

Fig. 6.7 Quantock harbours on the Bristol Channel coast. (Above left) *Detail from engraving by J. M. W. Turner (1820) of Watchet showing the wooden western retaining wall (see Fig. 1.11). The present stone jetty* (above right) *was rebuilt by the Wyndham family after storms in 1900 and 1903.* (Below) *Relicts of jettys built to protect Lilstock harbour built by the Acland Hoods (see also Plate 13A).*

wooden breakwaters and jetty) and complement this with an eastern pier. Together these arms gave an enclosed harbour capable of taking ships of up to 500 tons.

For most of this period Watchet was primarily a coal-importing port with South Wales ports as its main partners. But by 1828 a survey recorded a score of ships regularly trading with ports from London round to the main Irish and Scottish west-coast ports. The completion of the railway from Taunton reinforced Watchet's key role and this was further bolstered by the export of iron ore from the Brendon Hills from 1859. Specialist hoppers for discharging the ore into ships needed to be built on the western jetty. But the export boom was shortlived and declined from 1883 as mines closed. In the latter part of the century Watchet mainly imported coal and grain and exported flour and paper from its local industry. As the century ended both piers were to be damaged again by the great gales of 1901 and 1903.

To the east of Watchet, two small ports were established by the Acland-Hood family to serve its estates at St Audries and Fairfield. At Lilstock near Stogursey, a small harbour was established in the early eighteenth century and a cross-channel trade developed: coal was imported for domestic use on the Fairfield estate and for firing local limekilns. Pit props from estate forests were the main export but the harbour also had a social side, viz.:

> About 1832 Sir Peregrine Acland created a private road between his home at Fairfield and the cliff above the harbour, and built a wooden house there for his delicate only daughter. A promenade along the cliff became a recreation for local gentry, and in the 1860s and 1870s pleasure steamers plied between Lilstock, Burnham, Ilfracombe and Cardiff.[19]

In 1855 a customs post was established, a stone pier built parallel with the old quay, and a 'wooden awning with a butler's pantry' completed the picture. More prosaically, warehouses were built in 1866 and a decade later plans for a ship canal linking Lilstock via existing canals to Seaton on the English Channel coast was laid before the Admiralty. It never got built and by the end of the century the little harbour was in decline and effectively closed by World War I. A few signs of the abandoned port remain today (Plate 13A).

Apart from Watchet, Lilstock, and Combwich, coastal trade was ephemeral with small landing places in occasional use along the whole coast. In the west, seaweed was burnt at Cleeve Beach (now Blue Anchor) and exported to Bristol for use in its glass-making industry but this was cut off by the arrival of the Minehead railway in 1874. Steart, Shurton and Stolford in the east provided places for landing coal for domestic and limekiln use. All parishes along the coastal belt looked towards the sea and Stogursey records in 1803 that a local farmer owned three sloops used in coastal shipping. The river port of Combwich – perhaps the oldest of the Quantock ports and with a regular medieval trade with Ireland–gained new importance from its brick-and-tile industry from 1832. These were conveyed up the Parrett by small boats to be distributed onwards from Bridgwater and Langport.

Stolford, gained temporary importance as a possible starting-point for a channel-to-channel canal.[20] In 1822 work began on building a Taunton-Bridgwater canal to parallel the existing Parrett-Tone river navigation. By 1841 the canal was extended through Bridgwater to a newly-built dock where tidal gates allowed ships to be unloaded safe from the fast-running tides of the Parrett. This canal investment proved successful, mainly from the profits derived in moving coal. Coal had to be shipped by coastal freighters on a long, costly, and potentially hazardous voyage around Land's End from the exporting ports of South Wales to the importing ports of Devon, Dorset and Hampshire. To overcome this, various schemes for a channel-to-channel waterway across the isthmus separating Bridgwater Bay from Lyme Bay were proposed. Typical was that of Thomas Telford who surveyed a line for a ship canal (15 feet deep with thirty locks to take vessels of 200 tons) from Stolford on the Quantock coast near Stogursey to Beer on the Devonshire coast with a side-branch to Taunton. A harbour was to be constructed at Stolford and the first section of the canal cut across low ground to Combwich on the Parrett. Although an Act was passed in 1825, adequate finance was never forthcoming. Telford's was the most ambitious of several schemes for inter-channel canals put forward between 1768 and 1870, none of which was built.

VICTORIAN BUILDING AND RE-BUILDING

The Victorian period was one of great building activity in the Quantocks as elsewhere in England. There were several categories of building: ecclesiastical (with many parish churches remodelled and a new breed of nonconformist chapels); country houses; and village schools and other major public buildings including hospitals and asylums. The most important places referred to in the text are shown in Fig. 6.8.

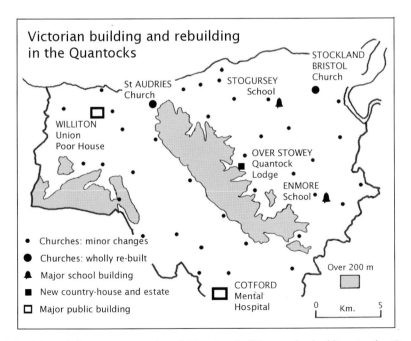

Fig. 6.8 Map of the main examples of Victorian building and rebuilding in the Quantocks. Churches, schools, country houses and major public buildings are identified.

Ecclesiastical buildings: churches and chapels

Few Quantock parish churches remained untouched by the Victorian religious urge to remodel and tinker with the medieval legacy. If the architectural excesses of vicars, rectors and their local patrons are sometimes deplored today, it is worth reflecting that many of the earlier structures would simply not have survived to the present without the newly leaded roofs, the restored stonework and the re-pointing which weather-proofed the old buildings. Here I'm on John Betjeman's side.

So though we rightly think of Quantock churches as medieval, many of their interiors were drastically altered during an eighty-year blitzkrieg. A roll call of changed interiors includes in time order Williton (1812 and again in 1859), Ash Priors (1833), Sampford Brett (1835-43), Over Stowey (1840) (see Fig. 6.9), Holford (1840s), Stogursey (1840-45), Nether Stowey (1849-51), Stockland Bristol (1860), Fiddington (1860), Kilton (1861), Cothelstone (1863-4), Stolford (1866), Tolland (1871), Charlinch (1886), and Otterhampton (1894). The names of John Norton (of Tyntesfield fame) and Richard Carver appear frequently in the list of architects. In many modified churches pulpits and rood screen between nave and chancel were a target for removal or rebuilding. Many stained glass windows were added but in most some medieval features such as fonts were retained.

But if altered churches from the Victorian period are abundant, wholly new churches are rare. The grandest is the parish church at West Quantoxhead (Plate 14A). Dedicated to St Etheldreda, from whose dedication the parish derives its

Fig. 6.9 The Victorian period was one in which many crumbling Quantock medieval churches were rebuilt or remodelled to make them sound and meet current aesthetic ideas. Complete rebuilding as with Norton's St Etheldreda at West Quantoxhead (left) was relatively rare. More common were major interior changes as with parish church of St Peter and St Paul at Over Stowey (right) as 'restored' in 1840 to the design of Richard Carver.

alternative name of St Audries, this was built by the Acland-Hood family as an integral part of the widespread development of the estate. Completed in 1856 to the design of the prolific John Norton, it has a church tower crowned by a small spire. It retains a simple twelfth-century font from its medieval predecessor. Other new Anglican churches were the starkly Victorian St Peter's (1868) at Combwich and Stockland Bristol.

The rise of nonconformity in the Quantocks also brought new buildings. Methodist churches were built in the villages of Bishops Lydeard, Combwich, Fiddington, Monksilver, Old Cleeve, Spaxton and Stogursey. Perhaps the finest example of this style is the Methodist chapel in Harbour Road, Watchet: built in 1871 close by the railway station it has distinctive coursed red sandstone, hamstone mullioned windows and a pitched slate roof. Its internal gallery provided space both for the largest Wesleyan congregation in the region and, a feature of Methodism, regular circuit-wide services and rallies.

Victorian country houses

Although not on the scale of earlier centuries, the Victorian period also left a legacy of country houses. It saw the building of one great country house and the extensive rebuilding of several others. At Over Stowey the first (and only) Lord Taunton, Henry Labouchere (1798-1869), bought much of the parish of Over Stowey from the Earl of Egmont and set about using part of the Baring fortunes (inherited through his mother) to build himself a baronial palace. 'Quantock Lodge', begun in 1857, was built in a neo-Tudor-style but with an

Fig. 6.10 Large non-ecclesiastical buildings were financed by both private and public wealth. (Left) The Gothic gatehouse built on the Nether Stowey road by Baron Taunton in 1857 for his Tudor-style Quantock Lodge. (Right) The Union Workhouse at Williton designed by William Moffat and built in 1838–40. It later became a hospital and is now being redeveloped for housing.

imposing Gothic lodge on the Nether Stowey road (Fig. 6.10 and Plate 14B). Unusually, the red warmth of so much Quantock building stone was eschewed, and a grey-green volcanic rock (Shalstein) from an estate quarry was used. The result was a sombre and forbidding building.

The Labouchere estate was serviced on the grand scale in line with its owner's wealth.[21] At its peak it had nearly forty servants, two thirds indoors and the rest (including a gamekeeper and assistants) outdoors. But the period of high living was to be relatively brief, at least as measured on a Quantock scale of ancient families. The estate was sold to Somerset County Council after World War I, the house later used as a TB sanatorium and then a school with the estate land leased by the Forestry Commission,

Other country houses were modified by the Victorians. In the northern Quantocks, Sir Peregrine Fuller-Palmer-Acland bought the St Audries estate in 1835 for his daughter Isabel and her husband. The medieval manor house was largely rebuilt over the next three decades in a Victorian Tudor style to the design of John Norton, the architect who had built St Audries parish church. The house was lit by its own private gas works with coal imported from South Wales from a small, specially-constructed harbour on the estate.

In the south, the First Viscount Portman took over the Warre estate at Hestercombe and demolished much of the old Tudor house. The Victorian mock-Italian villa which replaced it in 1875 was not a success and Pevsner allows the western approach as only 'relatively imposing' and the southern front as 'jumbled and featureless'.[22] It was to be rescued in the next century by its garden (see chapter 7).

These three houses – Quantock Lodge, St Audries and Hestercombe – were the most striking of many other examples of Victorian house building in the region. In 1808 Tainfield House was built by the Chapman family in Kingston St Mary in an Italian style, the name commemorating their sugar-growing estates at Tain in British Guiana. In 1821 Willett House, east of Elworthy, was built as a five-bay Georgian mansion to Richard Carver's design. The year 1860 saw both a many-chimneyed mansion at Stockland Manor and the towered house (the Grange) built to the design of Sir Gilbert Scott at Kingston St Mary. Finally, in 1875 Halsway House was rebuilt and extended in a Tudor style by the solicitor Charles Rowcliffe from 1875 (see Plate 5B and Fig. 7.12). Although by the end of the century the region had gained some fine buildings, it had lost others. Terhill House in West Bagborough parish was demolished in 1821 and only Jupiter survives of the ten classical statues which once graced the Slocombe estate there.

One feature which distinguished several Quantock country estates in the Victorian period was the extensive planting in estate grounds of exotic tree species. Some were to grow to form the massive trees which survived into the next century. Two special favourites were Cedar of Lebanon (*Cedrus libani*) from the eastern Mediterranean introduced into England as early as 1638 and Wellingtonia or the Giant Sequoia (*Sequoiadendron giganteum*) from the Sierra Nevada of California introduced in 1853. The Trevelyans of Nettlecombe Court were especially interested in tree introduction and pioneered the planting of uncommon Himalayan Cypresses (*Cupressa torulosa*) around 1824 into their grounds followed by a Tulip Tree (*Liriodendron chinense*) from central China towards the end of the century.

Village schools and public buidings

Before the Education Act of 1870, schooling in the Quantock villages was a somewhat hit and miss affair. In some, the church (including the increasing number of nonconformist churches) played a role through Sunday school teaching. In others the Dame school looked after the better-off children. But there were important exceptions. In Nether Stowey, Thomas Poole, the tanner friend of Coleridge (Chapter 1) started a village school in 1812 in Castle Street. In Enmore, his cousin who served as rector there for sixty years had founded a free school in 1810, which became a model for the National Schools movement and attracted countrywide interest. Rebuilt in 1848 and extended in 1888 it happily continues today (Fig. 6.11).

Several of the land-owning families took the lead in building schools in their parishes. The Trevelyan family at Nettlecombe established a school in the hamlet of Yard in 1819 to the design of Richard Carver. The Acland-Hoods

Fig. 6.11 The nineteenth century saw the widespread growth of village schools. Enmore village school was established by the rector, John Poole, in 1810. It was rebuilt in 1848 and extended in 1888. (Inset) Bicentenary celebration banner, 2010. A blue plaque near the main door marks its importance as a national educational landmark.

built two villages schools; the first in 1857 stands in the grounds of St Audries, the second in 1860 at Stogursey was built as a thank-offering by Sir Peregrine for the recovery from illness of his daughter Isabel. Both were designed by John Norton and have characteristic flourishes such as ornate chimneys and bellcots.

Two of the largest Victorian buildings in the Quantocks were publicly funded. At Williton a Union Workhouse was built on a monumental scale in 1838-40 to the design of William Moffat. It later became a hospital and was recently adapted again for multiple uses including housing (Fig. 6.10). A second institution, Tone Vale Mental Hospital, was built in 1897 as a grand complex of hospital buildings (including a church) at Cotford in the west of Bishops Lydeard parish.[23] Cotford remained the county's principal mental hospital until its closure in 1995. It now forms the centre for a 'new' village (see discussion in Chapter 8). Beside these two grand Victorian structures, other public buildings were smaller in scale: a new market hall for Stogumber around 1800 and new almshouses (through the generosity of the Acland-Hood family) for Stogursey in 1870.

POPULATION CHANGE

Population change reflects the many complex changes occurring in the Quantocks over this period. For the late eighteenth century we still have to rely on parish registers, but from 1801 on we can turn to the national decennial censuses.[24] For Somerset as a whole these show that its total population

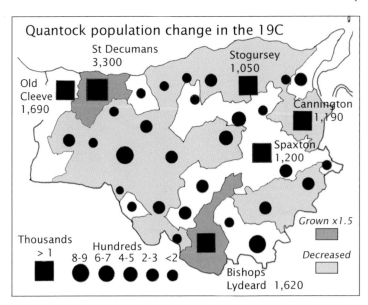

Fig. 6.12 Map of the distribution of growth and decline in the population of the Quantock parishes between 1801 and 1901. The population at the end of the century is given for the six largest parishes.

(270,000 in 1801) increased by about a half over the century. This was very slow by comparison with England and Wales which showed a threefold increase over the same period. If Somerset was a slow-growing backwater then, in demographic terms, the Quantocks were a backwater region within it. Over the whole century, the parishes which make up the Quantock region edged up by just ten percent, from a total of 15,500 souls in 1801 to only 17,100 in 1901.

Even this very modest growth was deceptive in two ways. First, in its geography (Fig. 6.12). The most populous Quantock parish was St Decumans, a large coastal parish which included the prospering port of Watchet and the growing transport nexus of Williton. This doubled its size. So if we take this single parish out of the account, then the rest of the Quantock region is stagnant with the same population overall at the end of the century as at the beginning. The map shows that of the remaining 38 parishes just eight showed a modest increase (a tenth or more). These included two special cases: Durleigh which had received an influx of population as Bridgwater's housing spread west and Bishops Lydeard which was boosted by the opening of a single hospital, the Somerset county mental hospital at Cotford (Plate 14E). Most other slow-growing parishes were large settlements such as Cannington and Old Cleeve which played a service role in relation to the smaller villages around them.

These cases apart, most parishes within the Quantock region shrank over the nineteenth century. As the graphs in Fig. 6.13 show, nearly half the parishes had fallen in population by more than one tenth of their 1801 size. These not only included the smaller and more remote hill parishes (such as Aisholt or Elworthy)

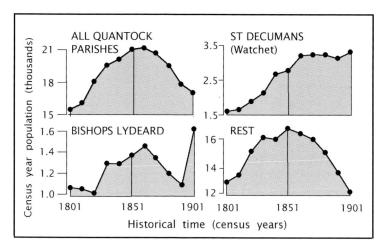

Fig. 6.13 Graphs of total population change over the nineteenth century for all Quantock parishes (upper left). When the growth of the two most populous parishes (St Decumans, including the town of Watchet, and Bishops Lydeard) are removed, the graph for the remaining rural Quantock parishes (lower right) shows a very marked decline over the century. Source: Data from Michin, 1906 (note 23).

but even substantial centres (Stogursey and Stogumber). As agriculture declined so emigration both to other parts of England and overseas to Canada and Australia took their toll of numbers.

But to look at just contrasts between numbers at the start and end of the century is too simple. For the Quantocks, it was a century of two halves. As agriculture and trade flourished, population grew by nearly a half to a peak in the 1851 and 1861 censuses, reaching almost 23,000. It was a total not to be reached again for another century. In the second half of the century, agricultural decline saw these substantial gains lost and population declined by a quarter from the mid-century highs. Indeed the second half was one of near universal losses with most parishes a third smaller in 1901 than at mid-century; the extreme case being Crowcombe which grew from 575 to 891 at mid-century only to drop to 374 by its end.

The curious story told by the population figures for the nineteenth century underscores the paradox of the whole of this period in the shaping of Quantock country. It began in the late eighteenth century with reform in agriculture, a brief mining boom in copper, a canal mania (which generally failed to affect the area) and the stirrings of new local industries. The next phase which lasted into the 1870s was one of rapid population growth, railway investment, major building enterprises with many churches remodelled and a few new country houses built. It culminated in the mid-century 'high farming' period when the Quantocks were at their peak of agricultural prosperity. And then the century ended with a whimper. The 1851 and 1861 censuses marked the high water mark. From then on farming was in decline, population was moving out to the towns (and even overseas).

Seven

THE LAST CENTURY OF CHANGE

In Memory of the Officers and Men
Of the 535th Anti-Aircraft Battalion-US Army
Stationed in Cannington
Prior to the Landing at Utah Beach on D-Day 6th June 1944
We Remember both Those who Served
And Those who Lost their Lives[1]

Plaques on the walls of Quantock parish churches are often worth pausing to read. In wandering around the lovely interior of St Mary's, Cannington, I had scanned the usual memorials to local landowning families (in this case the Bouveries of Brymore) and to long-serving Victorian vicars, when my attention was taken by the small plate on the north wall of the nave. It commemorates an American battalion stationed at Cannington in 1944 just prior to the chilling D-Day landings on Utah Beach. Links with Normandy in Quantock churches go back a thousand years but this time the direction of cross-channel invasion was the reverse of Duke William's landings.

This chapter concerns 'my' century (I was born and I suppose first saw the Quantocks over the edge of a pram in 1933) and the changes it wrought in the region. It starts with the Imperial certainties of the Victorian age and ends with the uncertainties of a country teetering on the edge of new, European-centred, waters. We begin the chapter with the Edwardian days when a rich Quantock family could afford to establish one of the great formal gardens of England and contrast it with the four bloody years of the Great War when all but one Quantock parish was touched by the death of one of its serving sons. The twenty inter-war years saw depression in the Quantock countryside with widespread forest planting changing the nature of the Over Stowey combes. It narrowly missed a Texas-style oil rush at Kilve.

World War II brought fewer deaths to Quantock Country but in other ways – as a training base, as a defensive line, as a refuge and even as a prison – the impact of war was even greater. Post-war years brought an ever increasing pace of change as tourism impacted, as conservation issues began their rise, as atomic power brought new landmarks onto the Quantock landscape, and as a new industrial agriculture replaced traditional farming. Finally, we draw together the threads of population changes over the century and see how this last century compared with those before.

AN EDWARDIAN INTERLUDE

In some ways 1897, rather than 1900, marked the end of the old century. That midsummer, Queen Victoria, who – as Tom Mayberry observes – had by then reigned for more years than most of her subjects had lived, celebrated her Diamond Jubilee.[2] Quantock parishes joined in the nationwide celebrations with enthusiasm. Jubilee Day, June 22nd, saw special services, luncheons and loyal speeches ended with the lighting of bonfires: more than a hundred were said to be visible from Cothelstone Hill that warm summer evening. Within four years, the Queen was dead and the new century began with a brief period in which the country seemed to hang between the certainties of the Victorian era and the turmoil which was to come.

In the quiet waters of the Quantocks, one event caught the spirit of the inter-vening Edwardian era most clearly. In 1903 the 2nd Viscount Portman's eldest son, made up for his father's sins in rebuilding the old Tudor house at Hestercombe (turning it into what Robin Bush describes as a 'Victorian mock Italianate villa'[3]) by commissioning a new garden for the area south of the house. To design it, he chose the greatest of contemporary garden designers, Gertude Jekyll, who – a follower of John Ruskin – had already completed a string of successful commissions and authored such bibles as *Home and Garden* (1900). Her own house and garden at Munstead Wood, Surrey, had become a shrine to the use of delicate colour in garden planning. For the 'hard landscaping' Portman commissioned the rising architect, Edwin Lutyens. Lutyens was later to gain international fame for buildings ranging from the Cenotaph in Whitehall to the imperial buildings of New Delhi. The combina-tion of the 60-year-old gardener with the 34-year-old architect was to produce one of the great gardens of England (Fig. 7.1). Work was begun in 1904 and completed by 1908.

Much of the character of the Lutyens-Jekyll garden comes from the skillful use of two local stones that outcrop in the southern Quantocks: the sandy, silver-grey sedimentary rock of the Morte slates and the dark pink diorite of igneous origin that outcrops on the estate.[4] An orangery of Somerset Ham Hill stone was added later. Below the south front of the house the land slopes away to give extensive views across the Vale of Taunton Deane to the Blackdown Hills. Here

Lutyens designed a suite of garden spaces on different levels using terraces and water channels to create the canvases on which Jekyll could paint her seasonally-shifting brushstrokes of colour. When restoration of the gardens was being started around 2000, two accidental discoveries uncovered Miss Jekyll's original planting designs. One set of plans were found stuffed in the drawer in the Hestercombe potting shed where they had lain undisturbed for seventy years; another set were found in the archives of the University of California at Berkeley, lodged there by a visiting American landscape architect.

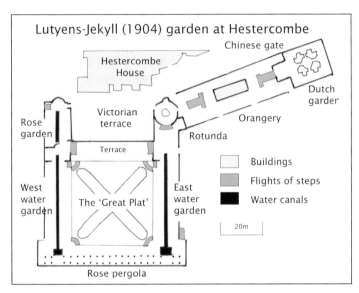

Fig. 7.1 The new century began on an optimistic note with the creation of one of England's great Edwardian gardens at Hestercombe. It combined the skills of two consummate artists: the gardener Gertrude Jekyll and the architect Edward Lutyens. (Above) Plan of the garden. (Below) Photo from the Dutch garden looking towards the orangery. Sources: Hestercombe Gardens, 2006 (note 4).

The original gardens were well-maintained by a large numbers of gardeners until 1914 when, as at Cornwall's Heligan (of 'lost gardens' fame), many went away to war. Since 2003 the gardens have been managed by the Hestercombe Gardens Trust and are open to the public. Today the beautifully restored Lutyens-Jekyll garden together with the restored eighteenth-century landscape garden lying north of the house (see Fig. 5.8) and the Victorian parterre attracts garden enthusiasts from around the world.

THE GREAT WAR AND ITS AFTERMATH

The Great War was to change the Quantock parishes – as it changed England – irrevocably. Not since the plague visitations of the medieval period had the area received such a sudden and unwelcome jolt to its demography. We look here at the immediate and then the longer-term impact.

Deaths in the Great War

The contrast between the Edwardian idyll and the next four years could not have been greater. The Great War, when it finally came, on a rainy Bank Holiday Monday in August 1914 was not to spare the Quantock country any more than other parts of the country. Lord St Audries spoke at West Bagborough the following day of 'the gravest crisis this country has known for one hundred years'.[5] Quantock men responded to the call to arms on a scale much greater than in previous conflicts including the Boer War. Most joined the army, notably the historic local regiments (the West Somerset Yeomanry and Somerset Light Infantry), others joined the navy and a few (like my father), the newly-formed Royal Flying Corps. The exact scale of war dead on the global scale will never be known with accuracy but exceeded 21 million.

Incumbents in each of the Somerset parishes were asked by the Bishop of Bath and Wells to report at the end of the war on the deaths of servicemen from their village.[6] Names were inscribed on vellum in a memorial book that remains in the cathedral library today. Of the more than eight thousand deaths recorded there, some 343 came from the Quantock parishes. Nearly one third of the deaths were of men from the Somerset Light Infantry: one of its battalions saw successive actions on the Somme and suffered particularly heavy losses around Beaumont Hamel in 1916. Aside from local regiments, Quantock men served and died in a wide range from the Army Cyclists Corps to the Burmah Rifles. The names of the dead include, somewhat surprisingly, men attached to overseas forces: the Canadian, Australian, New Zealand and even American Expeditionary Forces. Deaths in the Royal Navy are also recorded, particularly among men from Watchet. There was one woman on the list, Beatrice Elizabeth Stevens of Charlynch, a Quaker who died while serving in France in the Friends' Red Cross.

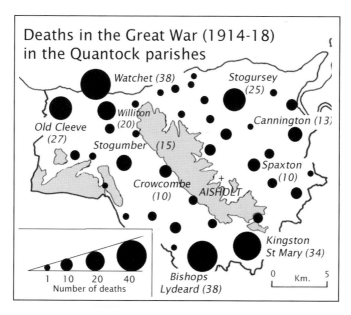

Fig. 7.2 The toll of death during the Great War (1914–18) varied across the Quantock parishes. Only the small parish of Aisholt escaped loss from the conflict. Circles indicate the relative numbers of deaths. Source: Data from Somerset County War Memorial, 1923 (note 6).

The spatial distribution of the deaths is shown in Fig. 7.2. Only one parish, the small hill village of Aisholt located in the southern Quantocks (see Plate 8A), escaped to join the tiny number of 'thankful parishes' scattered sparingly across the country. All the rest had grievous losses to report. While in half the parishes, five or fewer men had died, in a few numbers were much higher: Watchet and Bishops Lydeard (both with 38 deaths), Kingston St Mary (34), Old Cleeve (27), Stogursey (25) head the list. To some extent numbers were a function of the size of the parish with larger settlements showing the greater losses. But not entirely so: tiny Dodington with only 64 souls (in the 1911 census) lost four of its sons. Indeed we can roughly gauge the severity of loss, loss that is in purely demographic terms, by turning to the census. Those who served in the armed forces were largely drawn from the census age cohort 18–44 years and were overwhelmingly males. If we assume that the age distribution of the individual parishes (these are not given in the census) were the same as the three Somerset rural districts in which they lay, then we can begin to estimate relative losses. Quantock deaths in the Great War appear to represents one in fifty of its total population, but this rises to one in nine of the cohort of young males (18–44 years). The full horror of the war losses comes from the extreme cases; of those parishes mentioned above tiny Dodington lost one in three and Kingston St Mary one in five of this male age group. As a footnote we should note that even these losses are conservative since the War Office figures suggest the Wells book was incomplete.

Each country records its war dead: from France with its thousands of 'mourir pour la patrie' monuments to Australia with its avenues of white-barked gum trees. In the Quantocks, each parish church has its roll of honour often supplemented by a memorial cross erected by public subscription, some to a Lutyens design (Fig. 7.3). They remain a focus for Armistice Day services to this day. Less often a tablet or window records an individual tragedy. The grieving rector of Combe Florey placed a stained glass window on the south side of his nave:

> To the glory of God and in loving memory of John Edward Hyland, Lt. R.M.L.I. Killed in action leading and encouraging his men at Anzac [Cove] Gallipoli upon 10 May 1915. Aged 19 years son of rector of this parish. Erected by his sorrowing parents.

Losses were no respecters of rank or class and the death rates of officers, particularly junior officers, were often higher than the men in the companies they led. Such deaths had a wider impact on the local economy when taxation on inheritance via multiple death duties on estates had to be faced. The 1920s saw the largest sale of estate land in England's history and haemorrhaged value from many large Quantock landholdings. Such loss also brought a sharp drop in estate employment: the large numbers that we noted in the last chapter, notably as on Lord Taunton's estate at Over Stowey (Chapter 6), were not to be repeated.

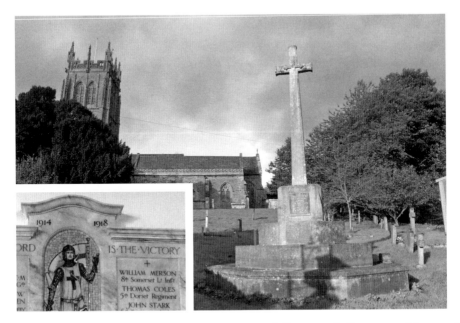

Fig. 7.3 Across the Quantocks, as across Britain and France and Commonwealth countries, memorials to the fallen of the Great War proliferated. The war memorial in the churchyard at Kingston St Mary with its 34 war dead. (Inset) Part of the memorial plaque to the fallen in Crowcombe parish church.

Aftermath: the inter-war years

The twenty years that separated the end of one world war from the start of another, is often portrayed as a drab one. In Britain it was a period when unemployment rose to one sixth of the working population, agriculture was in decline in the face of increasing imports, suburban ribbon development was snaking out from cities into the countryside. While Somerset was not immune from national woes, it fared somewhat better than the coalfields and highly-industrialized areas which took the brunt of the storm. For the Quantocks also it was a time of some change.

One of the consequences of the Great War was to draw heavily on the limited stock of native timber both for military and for civilian use.[7] In 1914, Britain

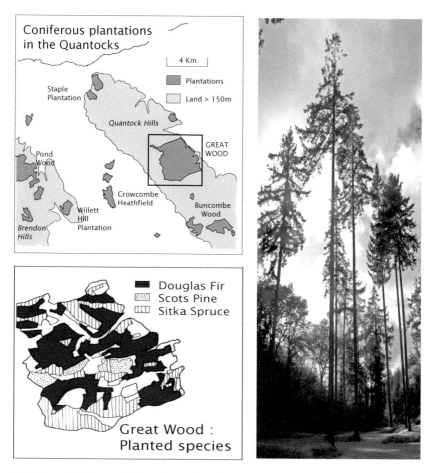

Fig. 7.4 The establishment of plantations of coniferous trees was common on steep, low quality land in the inter-war period. (Upper left) Map of coniferous plantations in the Quantocks. (Lower left) Map of main species planted by the Forestry Commission in Great Wood, Over Stowey parish. (Below) Old Douglas Firs in Rams Combe in the heart of the Great Wood plantation.

was 93 percent reliant on imported timber and by 1918 over 700 square miles of home woodlands had been felled. In Somerset this included 2,800 acres of woodland, mainly the oak woods which made up part of the Stanley estate in Over Stowey. In 1922 the Forestry Commission acquired some 1,600 acres of ridge and combe land in Over Stowey parish (Rams Combe, Keepers Combe and Cockercombe) (Fig. 7.4). It was largely scrubby cut-over estate woodland with a small acreage of neglected sheep-walk, with aggressive invasion by rhododendron scrub. In addition to the Over Stowey estate, a further 520 acres was acquired by the Forestry Commission in West Quantoxhead parish at the northern end of the hills in 1926. This was largely rough hill grazing that had previously formed the deer-park of the St. Audries estate.

From the outset, the Forestry Commission policy was to clear the area of scrub and replant with productive woodland species. But which species would best fit the Quantocks? Clearly not the native hardwood, oak, since this was far too slow growing (needing at least 120 years to mature). Quick-growing softwoods for pit props in the mining industry and constructional timber in the housing industry were in demand. A number of softwood species were tried with varying success. European larch (*Larix decidua*), brought into England from the Tatra mountains in the seventeenth century looked promising but proved a failure on all the sites tried. But two other imported species, this time from the Pacific northwest of North America did well: Douglas fir (*Pseudotsuga menziesil*) and Sitka spruce (*Picea sitchensis*) were both introduced *c*1830. Both produced excellent timber in the sheltered combes and lower hill slopes and as Fig. 7.4 shows were the main species planted in the Quantock Forest. Both proved less successful on the exposed seaward slopes of St Audries or the elevated ridges of the Over Stowey combes. In these tougher growing conditions, it was another imported species, the Corsican pine (*Pinus nigra*, var. *maritima*) first introduced from the Mediterranean *c*1760, that proved the more tolerant to exposure.

From the outset, the Forestry Commission's development programme ran into problems. Scrub clearance proved to be expensive, and in the case of Rhododendron infestation (see Fig. 8.4) almost prohibitively so. Once planting was started the young trees suffered from exposure to wind (especially on the exposed seaward slopes at West Quantoxhead). Even in sheltered areas all was not well. Cold air draining from the upper slopes accumulated in the bottoms of combes in winter causing frost damage. While disease and fire were a constant danger more critical was the extensive damage to young plantations from grazing animals: sheep, hill-ponies, and above all by deer. Given the high cost of erecting and maintaining deer-proof fencing, steps were taken to reduce the high deer numbers through culling. This aroused opposition from local bodies on both aesthetic and amenity grounds. Overall, the Commission's planting programme in the inter-war years proved over ambitious and — after the 'Geddes Axe' of 1934 slashed government spending – plans had to be reduced. Enforced savings in man-power meant that both maintenance and thinning fell behind schedule.

Early problems were eventually overcome and the inter-war forests today have reached a mature state. Improvements in forest roads in the combes cut extraction and shipping costs and, until the collapse of the mining industry in the 1980s, they formed a critical part of the product of the Quantock Forest. Already many inter-war plantings have been felled and new plantings have adapted to the revised brief of the Commission where recreational needs and catchment protection assumed a greater role. Hardwoods are now being planted along the forest edges to soften the hard edges of conifer blocks (Plate 16B).

A second major development was in mining. We noted in Chapter 2 that the cliffs on the northern coastal area are Jurassic in age and that some bands in this rock have a small oil content (Fig. 7.5). The presence of oil shales in the Kilve area had been reported in the geological literature as early as 1898 and in 1916 a trial boring near Kilve priory (see Fig. 4.10) probed their presence. In 1924 an engineer, Dr W. Forbes Leslie, assembled a syndicate of investors to form the Shaline Company to exploit the Kilve shales for oil production. Leslie gave a number of lectures on the potential of Kilve describing there as 'the most favourable ever met with in any oil shale field', viz:

No mining will be needed, The hills can be blasted down, great faces opened hundreds of feet high, and the rich oil fuel picked up by steam

Fig. 7.5 The 1920s saw a brief oil shale boom in the Kilve area. (Left) Liassic oil-bearing bands within shales in the Kilve cliffs. (Right) Remnant of retort for shale processing at Kilve beach.

shovels and loaded on the railway trucks for 3s per ton, as against 16s to 20s, the cost of mining coal.[8]

The quality of the ore was described as 'exceptional'.

Not surprisingly the local papers, notably the *West Somerset Press* (based at nearby Williton) and the *Bridgwater Mercury,* reported the lectures with a mixture of awe and enthusiasm. The bonanza atmosphere was further built up by the news that a new West Somerset Light Railway was to be built. This would consist of an initial eight mile line from Bridgwater (its terminal on the GWR line) to Stogursey followed by a three-mile section from Stogursey to the Kilve oil field (via Kilton). Finally a link from Kilve would run along the coast to the port and railhead at Watchet.

By May 1924 the new retort was finished and by July was up and running. The *West Somerset Press* was able to report with delight 'that the oil is there is proved beyond any question'. But that proved to be the last positive statement. On August 10th the plant dramatically closed. The Shaline bubble had burst and thereafter both local newspapers observed a stunned silence. What had gone wrong is still not known with certainty; the quality of the shale had probably been over-hyped and the costs of production underestimated. In the end not enough capital could be raised by the company to continue exploration and production at a time of general downturn and depression.

Today the only legacy of the short-lived 'South-Sea Bubble' is the lone, square-built, red-brick retort house some sixteen feet in height near Kilve Pill (Fig. 7.5). First of many buildings in the proposed refinery complex, it is still topped by a cast-iron chimney with a flange to carry away and condense the oily vapours. It stands as a reminder that some shales around Kilve do indeed retain some organic content derived from both from land vegetation and seaweed deposits in Jurassic times. But they are not as rich as those at Kimmeridge Bay on the Dorset coast. New gas-recovery technologies and a surge in gas prices could still turn the Kilve shales into oilman's country again.

A colourful portrait of the Quantocks in the late 1930s is given in one of my favourite maps, a battered, cloth-bound copy of Sheet 120 (*Bridgwater and Quantock Hills)* of the Land Utilisation Survey of Britain.[9] On it the hill country stands out in bright yellow as heath and moorland islands rising from a sea of meadow and grassland with the brown of arable land showing up more clearly in the Vale of Taunton Deane to the south of the hills. The survey was the brainchild of a geographer, L. Dudley Stamp of the London School of Economics, who enlisted the help of schools throughout the country in recording the use of land on every field on a six-inch map. In Somerset the work was completed under the direction of the Chief Education Officer over the years 1931-34. The Quantock map, like others for the country, was published at a scale of one-inch to the mile based on the original six-inch survey. The map showed fifteen types of land use in a mosaic of colours. For example, the dark green areas on the map representing areas of forest and woodland are divided into four categories of deciduous, coniferous, mixed and new plantations.

One major shift in land use in the inter-war period was the flooding of land for a reservoir. [10] The expansion of Bridgwater and the arrival of a new industry with high-water demands (the British Cellophane plant) meant that new sources had to be found. The Durleigh brook, a tributary of the River Parrett, was dammed in 1938 to create a lake covering 80 acres. Originally planned for water consumption, it has since become a major local centre for coarse fishing (particularly carp, roach, bream, perch, tench and pike), for sailing, and for wildlife conservation. Flooding continued after the war with the creation of the Hawkridge reservoir (opened 1963) though not on the scale of the Wimbleball and Clatworthy reservoirs on nearby Exmoor.

WORLD WAR TWO

The six years spanned by the second world war had a major impact on the Quantocks and deserve a separate section in any historical account. We look here at the casualties of war, the building legacy of defence works and encampments and the role of the region as both a prison and a refuge. Some of these impacts are mapped in Fig. 7.6.

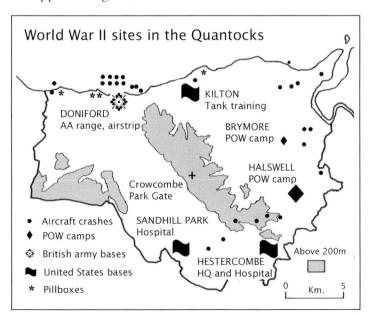

Fig. 7.6 The Quantocks in World War II. Map of major military and civil defense installations.
Source: Based on data in Hawkins, 1996 (note 1).

Athough in the Quantock parishes, the loss of life amongst service men and women in World War II was much less than in World War I, in many ways the impact was more immediate.[11] Unlike the Great War, aerial warfare meant that enemy bombing attacks included Somerset. Raids targeted the cities of Bristol and Bath and important industrial centres such as Yeovil. Where bombs fell on any of the Quantock villages this was probably due to faulty navigation or jettisoning load by German aircraft forced away from or unable to find their intended targets. Nonetheless, the recorded number of attacks was surprisingly high. At midnight on 1 August 1940, twelve bombs were dropped on the Nether Stowey area, three landing in the grounds of Over Stowey sanitorium. A week later two parachute bombs fell at Sampford Brett, possibly intended for shipping at Watchet two miles to the north. The heavy bombing of Bristol continued into 1941 with a small scatter of incidents in the Quantocks: isolated bombs and mines fell at Cannington, Elworthy, Kilve, Lydeard St Lawrence, Nether Stowey, Nettlecombe, Otterhampton, Spaxton and West Bagborough between June and September. Night bombing across the county petered out as Germany turned its attention eastwards towards Russia and a few bombs at Cannington, Over Stowey, and Bicknoller completed the record.

Given the rural character of the Quantocks, most bombs landed in open country and exploded without harm. But bomb disposal had its tragic consequences as at Blue Anchor in November 1942 when two members of a lifeboat crew were killed while investigating a parachute mine on a mudbank off the coast. Only two Luftwaffe planes crashed in the Quantocks: a Heinkel 111 at Crowcombe Heathfield after a Bristol raid and a Junkers 88 at Hestercombe. In contrast, 22 British and American planes crashed within the Quantock area, the largest number coming down around the coastal base at Doniford. Some of these were unmanned drones pulling gunnery targets that were shot down during aberrant artillery practice. But more serious crashes with loss of life also occurred: a Hurricane fighter at Dead Woman's Ditch (February 1942), a Spitfire near the Pines, Broomfield (October 1942) and a Wellington bomber flying into nearby Buncombe Hill (August 1943) killing five of the crew, were typical.

The thousands of troops stationed in the Quantocks needed accommodation. While existing hotels could be requisitioned for immediate military use and troops billeted on private homes (as in my parents' house), there was also a need for temporary encampments. Doniford had been a military camp since 1925 and was greatly expanded to house British troops (Fig. 7.7). The arrival of large numbers of American troops from late 1942 posed a still greater problem. A series of huts were built at Hestercombe.[12] Maps in the Somerset Record Office show that some forty barrack blocks were built in the grounds and one of these (with explanatory panels and photos) is preserved today. The House and the hutted camp was originally the headquarters of the British 8th Corps from

1940-1942, involved in both the defence of the southwest and later in planning warfare in Libya. With American entry into the war after Pearl Harbor in December 1941, the camp became the headquarters of U.S. 21st Army Group in the period leading up to the Normandy invasion. When the Americans left after D-Day the area had a brief civilian phase before being taken over by the womens' Auxiliary Territoral Service (ATS) for 1945–46 after which the hutted camp was abandoned. Nearby Sandhill Park became a British military hospital in 1940 and then a specialist U.S. neurological hospital for over one thousand patients (in 32 hutted wards) from 1942.

Less subject to decay than Nissan and like huts were the hundreds of concrete pillboxes built across the county between 1940 and 1943 as part of anti–invasion measures. These were not randomly spread but, as Fig. 7.5 hints, were arranged in distinct defensive lines either along the coast or as cross–country so-called 'stop lines'. Typical of the latter was the line running along the Quantock coast then from the estuary of the River Parrett south through Bridgwater and Chard

Fig. 7.7   During World War II many thousands of servicemen were located for brief periods throughout the Quantock parishes. Doniford was the original location of both an artillery training battery (upper left) from 1925 and subsequently an associated military air strip. A surviving hut in the grounds of Hestercombe House (upper right) was the home to both British and American troops between 1940 and 1946. After the war the Doniford camp (below) was cleared and converted to a holiday camp. Source: Photo of guns from Kit Houghton Collection, in Hawkins, 1988 (note 1), 95.

to Lyme Bay across the narrowest part of the southwest isthmus. Good examples of pillboxes can still be seen today near Blue Anchor and Watchet. Other examples of defensive works are the searchlight installations at Crowcombe Gate on the top of the Quantock ridge and anti-aircraft gun emplacements on the coast near Doniford.

Some of my most vivid boyhood recollections of war involved prisoners of war: an Italian prisoner with a diamond patch on his uniform teaching my mother a recipe for fried marrow flowers in our home kitchen; a young German prisoner with a circular patch (a music student at Heidelberg) playing J. S. Bach on the organ in our parish church. In the Great War, one Quantock country house – Sandhill Park – had housed German and Austrian officers and now a larger prisoner of war camp was established in another: the Halswell estate at Goathurst. A description of the Goathurst camp comes from an Italian prisoner, Nunzio Notaro, who was captured by the Australians at Tobruk in the 1941 Libyan campaign:

> The buildings at Goathurst were mostly of wooden construction … 20 yd long with bunks spaced every 4 ft – there were 64 of us accommodated in each. Security at Goathurst consisted of high fencing all the way round, but there were no watchtowers. Officers guarding us were billeted at Halswell House, and other ranks were in a barrack hut outside the compound. There were 700 prisoners in the camp at first, so one was lucky to get one bath a week.[13]

Notaro goes on to describe the farm work, Christmas toys made for local children, and even visits to the Odeon cinema at Bridgwater. Clearly Halswell was no Stalag Luft. All Italians were moved to Brymore in Cannington in the summer of 1944 when, after D-Day, German PoWs started arriving. After repatriation to Italy in 1946 Notaro returned to settle in the U. K.

The Quantocks were part of a rural area regarded as 'safe', and thus a destination area for children evacuated from war-damaged cities such as Bristol or London. At its peak in January 1941 the parish totals rose to between four and five thousand, dwindling away as city bombing eased and some children returned home. Most evacuees were children but included school teachers when whole schools were evacuated *en bloc*. Typical was the Poplar School of Navigation, evacuated from East London to join my own school at Durleigh on the eastern edge of the region. But evacuation was not just of children. Valuable items from churches in the City of London also found their way to the Quantocks. Lorry loads of furniture and fittings (from fonts to whole organs) were shipped from London to be stored in the vaulted cellars and outbuildings of St Audries School. Church bells from the historic City churches of St Bartholomew the Great, St Bartholomew the Less and from St Andrew Undershaft were stored for the duration of the war in the cloisters of Cleeve Abbey (see Fig. 4.9).

POST-WAR TRENDS

The nearer one gets to the present, the harder it is to see it in perspective. I have chosen to illustrate the second half of the last century by taking three leading themes to illustrate the forces of change: planning, settlement changes, tourism.

Planning, conservation, and the AONB

Although Somerset County Council commissioned a 'Somerset Regional Report' as early as 1932, rural planning in England largely sprang from the influential Scott Report a decade later on 'building and constructional work in rural areas'.[14] That and the Dower and Hobhouse reports on nature and landscape conservation lay behind the surge of optimism in the early post-war years that 'good planning' could avoid some countryside ills. The Town and Country Planning Act when it finally came in 1947 saw a crucial involvement of government, both at national and local levels, in shaping the future of rural England and with it the Quantocks. Thereafter, successive county-wide planning reports for Somerset (including the Quantocks as an integral part) applied the new legislation. As pointed out in Chapter 1, the laws which set up National Parks (including Exmoor) also led to the recognition – and special protection – of designated Areas of Outstanding Natural Beauty with the Quantock Hills as England's first AONB in 1956. From its base at Nether Stowey and now at Fyne Court, a small team of planners and field rangers have developed regular plans for monitoring, protecting and enhancing the 38 square miles of the Quantock Hills that comes under their care. Successive management plans (the latest for 2009-14) covering landscape, historic environment, local communities and the local economy have been drawn up by a Joint Advisory Committee which includes delegates from the county (Somerset), the districts (Sedgemoor, Taunton Deane and West Somerset) and interested parties.

Protection also came through the actions of specific government agencies with English Nature setting up sites of special scientific interest (SSSIs) on both biological and geological grounds. Three such areas are the 8,800 acres of Bridgwater Bay (1989), 6,200 acres of Quantock heathland (1970), and 1,800 acres of coastline between Blue Anchor and Lilstock (1971). English Heritage also provides capital grants to support remedial work on listed buildings of outstanding national importance. Non-government agencies in the form of non-statutory charitable bodies also have a key role. The National Trust (founded 1897) has acquired some critical parts of the Quantock Hills as well as the Coleridge cottage at Nether Stowey and Fyne Court (Fig. 7.8). The Landmark Trust charity (1968) has a mandate to rescue and restore buildings in distress and now owns two historic sites in the Quantocks (Stogursey Castle and Gurney Manor). Locally, pressure group such as the Friends of Quantock (1949) was set

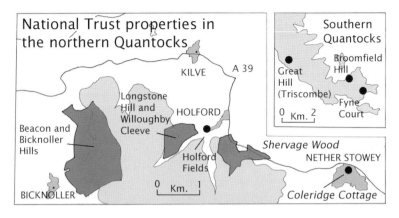

Fig. 7.8 Map of National Trust holdings in the northern Quantocks. Distinctive Trust emblem at Great Hill, near Crowcombe Park Gate (below).

up by volunteers as a charity to 'safeguard the landscape, natural beauty and amenities of the Quantocks, to oppose anything detrimental to peaceful natural beauty and to promote understanding, appreciation and responsible use of the Quantock environment'. It is represented on the AONB committee and is turned to by statutory bodies as a trusted voice on Quantock affairs. The Somerset Wildlife Trust (1964) aims to safeguard the county's wildlife and wild places for this and future generations but apart from Aisholt woods its nature reserves are largely outside the Quantocks in the Mendips and Somerset levels.

The biggest planning decision facing the region came in 1957 when central government allowed the siting of one of Britain's new family of Magnox nuclear power generators on the coast at Hinkley Port north of the village of Stogursey (Fig. 7.9).[15] It was to be the largest investment in the Quantock region in its history. Construction was begun in 1957 with the creation of a new five-mile road linking a refurbished river port at Combwich with the site. The first station began producing electricity in 1965. A second station (Hinkley B), using the

Fig. 7.9 Nuclear power first came to the Quantock coast in the 1950s. (Above) *Hinkley Point A and B viewed from the beach.* (Lower left) *Distant view of the two power stations from the Quantocks, see arrow.* (Lower right) *Three lines of pylons fan out southeast from the stations to connect to the National Grid.*

newer Advanced Gas Reactor (AGR) technology came on stream in 1976. Both stations are housed in stark, modernistic cubes and form the largest landmark on the Quantock coast (Plate 15A). Both stations are linked to the National Grid through major overhead power lines on great pylons that now stride across the Parrett like the machines portrayed in H.G. Wells classic *War of the Worlds*. Both Hinkley A and Hinkley B are now being phased out and we look in the final chapter at some of the questions raised by a proposed third reactor (Hinkley C) to replace them.

Settlement changes

In the late 1940s the Bristol geographer, Howard Bracey, carried out a unique Domesday-like study of village services in Somerset, Gloucestershire and Wilt- shire. It was based on coaxing a respondent (usually the village school mistress) in a thousand parishes to fill in his lengthy questionnaires.[16] On the basis of this survey, Bracey was able to develop a simple mapping of villages across the three counties. He divided the Quantock villages into four categories. Leaving Watchet aside as a town, he found there is just one 'first-order' village in the region (Williton) with its banks, schools, doctors, garages, and wide range of shops. Below this come three second-order villages: Bishops Lydeard, Nether Stowey, and Cannington with a more restricted service range. Finally come just two third-order villages: Stogursey and Stogumber. At the bottom are 30 villages with too few services to merit being classified. We get some sense of the range of shops in the late 1940s from Stogumber, which with a population of around 500 and five miles from the nearest-service centre (Williton), had three shops:

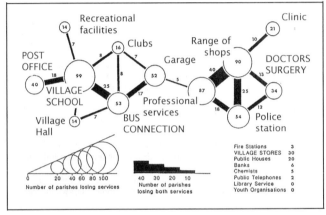

Fig. 7.10 Local loss of services between 1950 and 1980 in all Somerset parishes showed a close intercorrelation (left) *between the different sevices. A general store under the Spar franchise* (right) *at Cannington today. Source: Haggett, Mills & Morgan, 1983 (note 16).*

All were of a general store type. Two had counters for boots and shoes, two for hardware, two for newspapers and magazines, one for the mainly women's and children's clothing, while the garage sells bicycles, radio sets and household electrical goods.[17]

Bracey's study was repeated thirty years later by Liz Mills. Her follow-up survey showed how factors from growth in car ownership to supermarket shopping (still then at an early phase of growth) had speeded a shrinkage in village services. Over the intervening years, a quarter of villages had lost their village schools. Her most important finding was to demonstrate the close inter-linking of service loss. As Fig. 7.10 shows, closure of one facility (a village school) was closely linked to loss of others (e.g. post office and bus connections).

Alongside such village change has gone a series of other community changes such as diocesan church reorganization (see discussion in Chapter 8). This is not confined to Anglican churches: in the Quantocks nonconformist churches have lost over half their premises within the author's lifetime.[18] Local hostelries are close to the heart of many Quantock villages, hosting skittle matches and quizzes and providing a meeting place for the village cricket club or dramatic group. Fig. 7.11 plots the pubs still in operation in 2010 although since that date

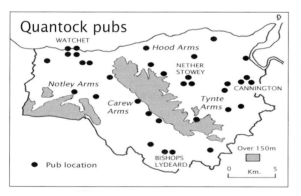

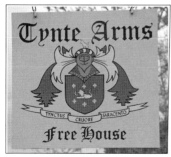

Fig. 7.11 Map of Quantock taverns at the end of the century (above left). *Many of the inn names are of some antiquity and mark the names of local land-owning families: The Hood Arms, Kilve; the Tynte Arms, Enmore; the Notley Arms, Monksilver; the Carew Arms, Crowcombe.*

two more have closed. Many have long histories with the pub name marking links with the families that shaped so much of Quantock life.

The net effect of population loss and services loss has been to differentiate the Quantock villages. Large ones on the main highways (e.g, Cannington, Bishops Lydeard) have tended to grow; the smaller ones on minor roads (e.g. Aisholt, Broomfield, Tolland) have tended to stagnate. This process has been reinforced by successive planning reports with their emphasis on a 'key village' strategy. The realities of school provision or main drainage has tended to allow approvals for housing development in some villages over others. The largest housing development in the region has been in the south of the region where the closure of the Tone Vale mental hospital (Plate 14E) in the 1990s has allowed an entirely new village, Cotford St Luke, to be built. So far a new community school and over 800 houses have been built or converted from old hospital premises and in 2011 the area split from Bishops Lydeard to form a new parish.

One element in the settlement pattern which we noted in Chapter 5 was the richness of the Quantocks in small and medium-sized country houses and their associated parklands. A century ago most of the houses remained in private occupation, sometimes by the same families that had constructed them: the Lutrells at the Court House, East Quantoxhead, the Acland-Hoods at Fairfield near Stogursey, and the Wyndhams at Orchard Wyndham near Williton are outstanding examples. But for most houses, that situation has now changed. In the early years of this new century, family occupation is the exception, and retention by the same family has almost (but happily, not quite) ceased. The question arises as how to protect these superb but costly-to-maintain structures which were built at a time when labour was cheap.

In some cases houses have been successfully adapted for institutional use. Five houses were leased or bought and adapted by Somerset County Council. At Cannington the Priory was leased to Somerset County Council as the core of an agricultural and horticultural college in 1919 and, after World War II, Brymore House was adapted as a farm school. Kilve Court, the three-storeyed mansion built in 1786, was taken over by the council in 1967 and continues in use as a residential education centre. It is well used by visiting schools and teaching courses make heavy use of the Quantock environment. Hestercombe House was also leased and then bought by Somerset County Council after the death of Lord Portman's widow in 1951. Used as the headquarters of the county fire service from 1975 it is now an outstanding centre for studying garden history. Quantock Lodge, Lord Taunton's estate at Over Stowey, was sold in 1920 on the death of his daughter, Mary Stanley. The house and immediate grounds were used by the county health service as a sanatorium for TB patients from 1925-62, then sold on for use as a private school until 2000.

Fig. 7.12 Finding a role for large country houses became a problem in the post-war period. Halsway (pronounced 'Halsey') Manor was in place by the Domesday survey and owned by the Halsway family from the twelfth century. Largely rebuilt in Tudor style by solicitor Charles Rowcliffe from 1875 it has since 1963 been the national centre for folkdancing and folksong.

At Broomfield, the rump of Fyne Court (partially destroyed by fire in 1894) and its surrounding estate was left to the National Trust by John Adams in 1967. It was the headquarters of the Somerset Wildlife Trust from 1974 and is now the centre for the Quantock AONB. Nettlecombe Court on the northern fringes of the Brendon Hills remains in family ownership but was briefly leased for use as an independent preparatory school. In 1967 it became the Leonard Wills Field Centre run by the Field Studies Council. As such it offers leisure and professional residential training courses in all aspects of wildlife ecology and environmental matters attracting both individuals and school, college and university groups. Halsway Manor lies in a sheltered location at the western foot of the Quantocks (see Fig. 7.12). In 1965 the Halsway Manor Society was set up to run the manor as a residential folk centre. Today, as the England's National Centre for Traditional Dance, Music and Song it uniquely offers a wide range of residential courses and welcomes visitors to open days.

Finding a role for great country houses in the Quantocks continues to be sought. St Audries House and Halswell House now serve as very grand wedding and conference centres and Alfoxton is under adaptation. Hill House, at Otterhampton, has served since 1976 as a Christian Youth conference centre while other faiths have shown interest in other houses. The future of the great mansion at Crowcombe Court remains uncertain. One sad footnote to the country house question came in November 2011 with the destructive fire at Sandhill Park in Bishops Lydeard parish. Abandoned and boarded up for more than a decade, vandals broke into the house and started a fire. By the time the fire was extinguished, a wing had been gutted and the roof space badly burnt.

Sample 1 km x 1 km square

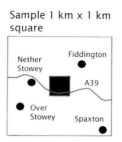

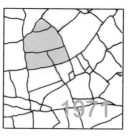

Fig. 7.13 Loss of field boundaries and increase in field sizes became acute with mechanized farming in the post-war years. (Above) Sample 1km x 1km square near Nether Stowey showing loss over a twenty-year period. (Below) View north over the area in 2010 showing further losses, Source: Sedgemoor Distrct Council, 2003 (note 19).

Outside the great estates, farms have been showing major changes. Small, mixed farms, once the signature type for much of the Quantocks lowlands have become increasingly uneconomic. Farms have merged and field sizes have grown to meet the needs of expensive tilling and harvesting equipment (see Fig. 7.13).[19] The 1980s saw a shift towards conservation of farmland and the introduction of a series of 'agri-environment' schemes. As European Farm Policy changed so new crops (notably maize, rape and sunflowers) have been tried and specialized poultry farms have developed as around Steart. In a few cases a wholly new landscape has emerged as with the current vineyard at Oatley, near Cannington, a reminder that mention of local vineyards occurs fitfully as early as late-Saxon charters (on land near St Decumans, Watchet).

Tourism

One prominent marker on the west Quantock coastal road is the distinctive high masts and low buildings of the BBC wireless station at Washford opened in 1933. Today the site has been adapted as the 'Tropiquaria' centre that houses, in addition to a small wireless museum, a range of all-weather entertainment for children built around a collection of exotic birds and animals. The change is symbolic of the switch of the Quantocks in the post-war period towards a

Fig. 7.14 With the closure of the commercial port of Watchet in 1992 a marina for pleasure boats at Watchet was opened. The Esplanade on its southern side has recently been redeveloped with statues (below) commemorating the ports maritime links through Coleridge's 'Ancient Mariner' and a local sea-shanty singer, 'Yankee Jack'.

tourist economy. This is particularly concentrated along a six-mile stretch of the northern coast from Blue Anchor to St Audries Bay. Here a succession of coastal sites – Home Farm, Warren Farm, Helwell Bay, Doniford, St Audries, Perry Farm – offer family accommodation at various levels from permanent caravans and trailerhomes through to camping sites. The largest of them at Doniford (Plate 13D) was converted from the former military encampment. A major coastal tourist development (the Butlin's holiday camp at Minehead, opened 1962) lies just west of our region and its estimated 400,000 visitors each year add to tourist demand in the Quantocks.

Watchet sits in the centre of this tourist strip and its shops, pubs and museums gain greatly from seasonal trade. This has compensated in part from the ending of its historic role as a commercial harbour with the construction of a marina in 2001. This provides accommodation for up to 240 sailing vessels or motor boats (up to sixty feet in length), both berth holders and visitors. The marina has been designed as a floating harbour set within the historic harbour with access limited to a period around high tide. The Esplanade bordering the harbour on its southern side was remodelled in 2008 and contains two recent statues celebrating the artistic history of the harbour, Coleridge's 'Ancient Mariner' and the shanty-singer 'Yankee Jack' (Fig. 7.14), while the western jetty records the history of iron-ore shipping. Controversy rumbles on over development of a major blocks of flats on its eastern side.

In 1962 British Railways published its controversial report on the *Reshaping of British Railways* (the 'Beeching Report'). One of the predictable casualties was the Quantock's branch line, from Taunton to Minehead. Despite vigorous local campaigning the line was closed to freight in 1964 and to passengers in 1971.[20] In the same year a Minehead Railway Preservation Society held its first meeting in Taunton and a West Somerset Railway Company formed to acquire the line and run it privately as a heritage railway. The line was purchased by Somerset County Council and leased to the new company. The new line opened in stages starting at the Minehead end; to Blue Anchor (1976), on to Williton later the same year, with the final connection through to Bishops Lydeard (1980) (Fig. 7.15). A new station was opened at Doniford Halt in 1987 to serve the holiday camp at Helwell Bay. Bishops Lydeard remains the terminus today (with a connecting bus service on to Taunton) but plans to link through to Norton Fitzwarren junction on the main line remain under discussion. Today the railway is the largest tourist attraction in the region with a loyal and dedicated following that range from local volunteers

Fig. 7.15 The restored West Somerset Railway. (Left) WSR poster designed by Peter Barnfield. (Right) Photo by author of engine climbing incline to Kentsford Farm crossing.

through to international enthusiasts. The fact that Crowcombe Heathfield station has been used for filming from the Beatles *Hard Day's Night,* through *Land Girls,* to *The Lion, the Witch and the Wardrobe* adds to the draw of the line.

The railway, in common with other tourist attractions, faces a seasonal concentration of visitors. Most demand occurs in the Easter – September period (with peaks in public and school holidays) and steps have been taken to 'stretch' the tourist season by running special attractions in early autumn). Similar moves have been made by local authorities to reduce the spatial concentration of visitors into the Blue Anchor – St Audries coastal strip. A West Somerset Coast Path (WSCP) was opened in 2006 as a way-marked trail from Stert Point in the east to link up with the start of the South West Coast Path (which runs via Cornwall around to Dorset) at Minehead. Stert is also the start of the north-south Parrett Trail which links Bridgwater Bay with Lyme Bay in Dorset. Other tourist strategies to spread demand more widely over the region have been put forward by both the Quantock AONB and local authorities and are discussed in Chapter 8.

POPULATION CHANGES OVER THE CENTURY

As in previous chapters, we look finally at population changes across the Quantock region as a way of drawing together overall changes in economy and landscape. In the nineteenth century the region started at 15,500 in the 1801 census, surged to a mid-century peak of 23,000 and then fell back to 17,300 in 1901. No such boom and bust marked the twentieth century. Numbers grew slowly but steadily in the first half to regain its previous 1850s peak by the 1971 census, surging again to reach 28,600 in the 2001 census. Although the gain of 65 percent over the whole century was rapid in Quantock terms, the gains were proportionately less than both the historic county of Somerset and the rest of England.

Geographically, the spatial pattern repeated the variations of the previous century: eight parishes more than doubled in size, including such large centres as Watchet, Bishops Lydeard and Cannington. The parish with the greatest increase was Durleigh with its fourfold growth reflecting the westwards overspill of Bridgwater housing reinforced by boundary changes. Four in every ten Quantock parishes lost population. As Fig. 7.16 shows, the losing parishes were mostly grouped in the southern Quantocks (Broomfield, Cothelstone, Enmore, Kingston St Mary and Spaxton) and a swathe of parishes in the Brendon Hills running from Elworthy south to Combe Florey).

In addition to basic population counts, the 1981 and 1991 national censuses collected data on many aspects of economic activity, household tenure and amenities, household composition, car ownership, dwelling type and ethnicity. Some of these data were collected on a ten percent sample basis and so not

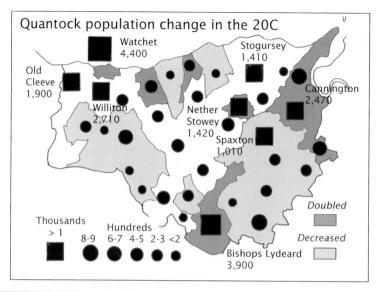

Quantock population change in the 20C

Watchet 4,400

Stogursey 1,410

Old Cleeve 1,900

Cannington 2,470

Williton 2,710

Nether Stowey 1,420

Spaxton 1,010

Doubled

Thousands
> 1

Hundreds
8-9 6-7 4-5 2-3 <2

Decreased

Bishops Lydeard 3,900

Fig. 7.16 Quantock population change in the twentieth century. (Above) *Map of settlement sizes at 2001 and trends over the century for each parish.* (Below) *A view of the fastest growing settlement in the Quantock region, Cotford St Luke, located in the southern part of Bishops Lydeard parish five miles from Taunton. It was founded when Tone Vale Hospital (Plate 14E) was closed in the 1990s; the old buildings were converted and new housing estates built in the hospital grounds. By 2012 Cotford was large enough to have a ten-class school and parish council. The hospital church in the background is now a public house. Photo by author*

published at the civil parish level but for aggregated 'wards'.[21] The twelve rural wards which cover the Quantocks are shown in Fig. 7.17: while the Quantock boundary does not exactly match ward boundaries the overlap is sufficiently small to be ignored. In relation to England, the Quantock population in the

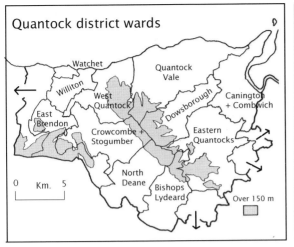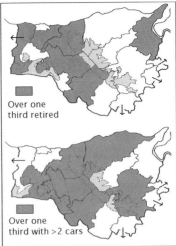

Fig. 7.17 Recent statistics for the Quantock area have grouped the original civil parishes into district wards (left). Map of the fifteen Quantock wards with areas with higher retirement and higher car ownership shaded (right). Source: Adapted from data published by the Somerset County Council, 1991 (note 21).

1990s tends overall to be (a) more elderly (a quarter of pensionable age and a third retired) and (b) relatively well-off (three quarters owning their own homes, a third having two or more cars, and nearly a third being in census terms 'upper class' [i.e. in Class I and II on a five-class scale]).

But this bland view across the whole Quantock region conceals major geographical variation. Thus the 'upper class' proportion varies fourfold over the region, from 51 percent (Crowcombe - Stogumber ward) down to 12 percent (Watchet). If we group several indicators of wealth together then it is tempting to see a 'prosperous and retired' belt (a rural Tunbridge Wells, even) running east west across the Quantocks from East Brendon ward, through Crowcombe & Stogumber and North Deane to Eastern Quantocks. The region's largest settlement, Watchet, stands apart with a younger population, lower car ownership, a fifth of its housing local-authority rented, and unemployment running at ten percent. Its neighbour, Williton, shares some of these indicators though as the administrative centre of West Somerset District it has shown better employment growth than its sister settlement. Wards nearer to the two main towns, Bridgwater and Taunton, show a more marked commuter profile with a higher working population and younger age profile.

The twentieth century began with certainties and ended with doubts. The certainty of the old historic county of Somerset was shattered in 1974, when the northern third beyond the Mendips was carved away to form a new Avon county with the southern part of Gloucestershire. Second thoughts in 1996 created two new 'Somersets' (North Somerset and Bath & North East Somerset) but left the old rump county unchanged. The two most important changes from the viewpoint of our region were contradictory; the formal; recognition of its landscape value with the creation of the Quantock Hills Area of Outstanding Natural Beauty in 1956 was a high point, one somewhat overshadowed by the huge investment in the two atomic reactors at Hinkley Point from 1957 which raised new environmental issues and dramatically altered the eastward view from those same hills. There was much to celebrate (like the establishment of the AONB and the saving of the West Somerset Railway) and a few to lament.

Eight

QUANTOCK FUTURES

The picture of the mind revives again:
*   While here I stand, not only with the sense of*
Of present pleasure, but with pleasing thoughts
*   That in this moment there is life and food*
For future years: And so I dare to hope,
*   Though changed, no doubt, from what I was when first*
I came among these hills.

William Wordsworth, *Lyrical Ballads* (1798)[1]

William Wordsworth had left Alfoxton with his sister in the summer of 1798 and whether these lines were written recalling the Quantocks is a matter for debate. But it suits my sense of symmetry to return to a poet we first met in Chapter 1. His reference to 'life and food for future years' fits the mood of this final chapter exactly for here we pause at a cross-roads in the evolution of this most English of regions. For a geographer who holds that, *pace* global warming, we may not be more than a millennium or two from the start of the next ice age it is not wise to try and look ahead too far.[2] But even over the next decade or two, changes are affecting the Quantock region that will be at least as challenging as any that have moulded it over the long history traversed in the previous chapters.

But like Wordsworth 'I dare to hope'. I'm writing this final chapter by a mill stream that drains down from the Quantock Hills through the broad meadows of Cannington parish. Here at Currypool, a settlement recorded in the Domesday book, is the complex of waterways and leats that have turned gener-ations of mill wheels for a thousand years. The waters now flow each side of the small log cabin where we're staying and here – in the first decade of a new century – the latest mill wheel still turns. Only this wheel is connected not to heavy grinding stones but to a modern generator that creates the electricity which powers the electronic laptop on which these words are being written.

Surplus power from the mill is being passed on to the National Grid to supplement the slowly dying nuclear generators at Hinkley Point.

In this final short chapter, I turn to the future of this Quantock region and try to identify some issues it faces as it encounters the challenges of a new century. Many of the parishes that make up the region issued their own reports to celebrate the millennium.[3] Here we identify just a few common themes. We look first at the Quantock Hills with their sensitive and fragile habitats of moorland and woodland. How do we protect the iconic landscape that led to its adoption as England's first AONB? Then as tourism climbs in importance in the region's budget, how do we maintain the balance between encouraging visitors while avoiding it becoming a theme park? And what of the subtle hierarchy of Quantock villages where – to judge from crumbling churches, closed schools, and thinning pubs and garages – many of the smaller ones are dying. Can a new settlement pattern be envisaged? And how do we deal with the new cuckoo in the Quantock nest? Can and should a third reactor at Hinkley Point be added to the present nuclear mix and are there other (local) schemes that could raise the output of electric power? Rather than leaving the chapter at a point of controversy, I close the book with a final Quantock walk to convince myself (and readers) of that quiet beauty which gives point to all our discussions.

FIVE QUANTOCK ISSUES

In the early years of the twenty-first century, many issues are troubling this quiet corner of England. I choose here just five, some parochial some global, as illustrations. This is my list: others would have chosen differently.

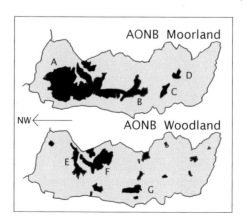

Fig. 8.1 Two iconic elements of the landscape of the Quantock Area of Outstanding Natural Beauty. Open heather moorland and rough grazing (above) and combe-side and hillside broadleaved woodland (below).

Issue one: Protecting the upland moors

Most of the higher areas of the main Quantock ridge are covered in open moorland (see Fig. 8.1). Extensive since late Mesolithic times this open area has been systematically reduced over two millennia of cultivation, mainly by intakes around the margins, and by afforestation in the combes. Their significance as an endangered habitat is reflected in the fact that (as we saw in Chapter 7) all are within the AONB remit, some have been designated as sites of special scientific interest (SSSIs), while others are in National Trust ownership.[4]

Looking across the heathland today one sees not a uniform landscape but a patchwork of vegetation. Low shrubs dominate, with the balance of species in any patch reflecting environmental controls: soils and geology of the site, exposure to wind and rain, local topography (both slope and aspect are critical), and recent history. Over many acres common heather (*Calluna vulgaris*) is the dominant plant with whortleberry, bell heather, cross-leaved heath, and common and western gorse also prominent. All are lime-hating plants which thrive in the peaty, acid soils of Quantock tops. Such heathland is seen at its best in late summer when the intermingling of the mature heathers with the gorse gives a stunning purple-yellow palette of colour and a harvest of whortleberries can be gathered. Among the low shrub, moths (including the Silver Y and Emperor) dart while the sounds of whinchat, stonechat, meadow pipit, and skylark can be heard.

But as Fig. 8.2 shows, this classic heather moorland is highly vulnerable, held in place only by a particular (and easily upset) group of forces. Left undisturbed, the heathers would undergo natural change, becoming woody, overshadowed by

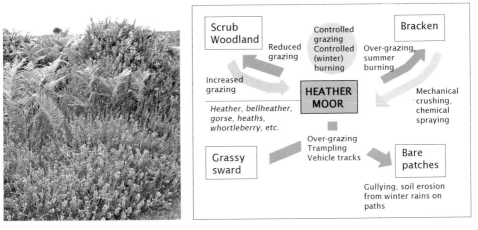

Fig. 8.2 The mosaic of species which make up heather moorland (left). The moorland is only kept in existence by a complex series of factors (right) which include grazing and controlled burning (swaling). Without these the moorland would gradually convert to scrub woodland.

gorse, and eventually invaded by tree species (hawthorn, holly, silver birch and mountain ash in the early stages; oak in the longer run). Invasion by bracken is another threat, one increased by overgrazing by herbivores (deer, sheep, horses and cattle). Accidental blazes in summer also tip the balance towards bracken, fire totally destroying a heather stand but knocking back bracken only for a single season: bracken rapidly recolonizes through its tough underground stems.

Maintaining heather moors demands sensitive adjustment of environmental controls. Winter-burning (locally called 'swaling') of small sections of heather is one technique. For ecological reasons it is carried out in winter and restricted to areas no larger than ten acres. Each block is burnt on a fifteen-year rotation cycle both to ensure good grazing and to conserve wildlife habitat. Limiting the

Fig. 8.3 Examples of grazing pressures. (Above) *Part of a small herd of Exmoor ponies on Cothelstone Beacon.* (Below) *Winter snow on the open moorland has forced this herd of sheep down to graze in the sheltered undergrowth below the oak woodland at Lady's Edge.*

number of grazing animals is another adjutment (Fig. 8.3). The sixteen square miles of common land on the Quantocks support grazing rights for up to 9,000 sheep, 230 ponies, 160 goats and 140 head of cattle but actual numbers are kept well below those figures. Local overgrazing will push plant distributions towards either a grassy sward or towards bracken depending on other local factors. Controlling bracken invasion is both difficult and expensive: mechanical crushing and chemical spraying are feasible but both need to be conducted in late spring/early summer and so tend to disturb wildlife at a critical time of the breeding year. The outcome of spraying experiments by Natural England on Aisholt Common and the use of helicopters for spraying seem to have given positive results with reinvigoration of both grass and heathland species.

Protecting the bird fauna of the Quantocks remains important. Regular surveys by the AONB service with the Royal Society for the Protection of Birds (RSPB), allow a good picture of breeding bird populations to be built up. Measured in terms of territories or pairs, densities range from the relatively common meadow pipit and linnet down to the rarer whinchat and redstart with one sixth as many breeding pairs. Some birds favour the hill tops (e.g. skylark and whinchat), some the valleys (e.g. linnet and yellowhammer), and some the woodland edge (e.g. redstart and willow warbler).

Riding and walking on the hills causes relatively little damage as long as numbers are low but the increasing use of four-wheeled vehicles and, to a lesser degree, mountain bikes is extending the area of bare ground with implications for accelerated erosion in winter storms. Many of the single-track paths I followed as a boy have now grown rutted to many yards wide by my old age.

Issue two: Combes and woodlands

Although, many of the steep-sided combes that surround the Quantock ridge have small patches of woodland, it is the long branching combes on the eastern side that have the most continuous cover (see Fig. 8.1). If we except Great Wood and Staple Wood with their coniferous plantations (discussed in Chapter 7), the dominant Quantock species is a type of oak, sessile oak (*Quercus petraea*).[5] Historically, this oak was widely planted for its twin advantages in producing tanning bark and high-quality charcoal, both major industries in the combes up until 1900. On the slopes oak woods were coppiced every ten to fifteen years to provide these two products, while in the valley bottoms single stems were left to grow as standards to provide timber and firewood. Other trees include rowan, birch, holly and hazel (in the drier combe sides) and alder and willow (along the watercourses and combe bottoms). Ashwoods are common on the limestone areas as around Aisholt and there is a fine stand of beechwoods on the slopes around Cothelstone. Beech was also used as a boundary marker on the high banks around enclosures in the hill country (Plate 4).

Fig. 8.4 Two factors in woodland management which have proved difficult to control. (Left) The beautiful but aggressive Rhododendron ponticum. (Right) Red deer were common on the hills into at least the late medieval period and were reintroduced only in the late nineteenth century.

One problem facing the woodlands today is invasion by Rhododendron (Fig. 8.4). *Rhododendron ponticum* is an exotic introduced from Turkey in the late eighteenth century and popular with Victorian landowners for its ornamental value, both its glossy leaves and attractive mauve flowers in late spring. Three problems occur with this species: fast growth allows it to out-compete most native species; dense foliage allows little light to penetrate through its canopy; and toxins make it unpalatable to most grazing animals. This, plus its ability to spread by both seed and lateral roots, makes it a formidable invader in the Quantocks of both wooded areas and their heathland margins.

A second problem comes from high deer populations and their effect on trees through grazing and bark stripping.[6] Red deer (*Cervus elephas*) probably migrated into England following the retreat of the ice sheets some 10,000 years ago. By Norman times growing human populations with woodland clearance probably confined them to the Royal forest of the south-east Quantocks and to estate deer parks. In 1862 red deer were reintroduced from Exmoor for hunting. After later deer releases, the Quantock Staghounds were set up in 1901, disbanded during the war but revived when several stags were brought in from Sussex herds. Traditional hunting with a full pack of hounds continued until 2005 when legislation restricted it to a more limited form of 'exempt hunting'.

Today, red deer numbers on the Quantocks have grown substantially. Annual spring counts by the Quantock Deer Management Group have shown numbers varying between roughly four to nine hundred with a steady increase over the last decade. Numbers are currently at high levels and above the 450 threshold for a healthy deer population (given the land area and grazing available). In the absence of natural predators, culling by hunting or shooting is necessary to control numbers. Red deer problems are exacerbated by the increasing number of other deer species.

Deer have both positive and negative impacts on the Quantocks. On the positive side, they are symbolic of the hills and to catch a glimpse of a herd of hinds with their young (groups range in size from ten to sixty) or to hear the 'belling' of the stags during their autumn jousts is to catch the spirit of the hills. Views on hunting differ sharply but deer provide a renewable source of venison and sustain employment through both the hunt and the equestrian economy. On the negative side, deer at high densities cause damage to young trees through grazing, antler rubbing and bark stripping. Food shortages in winter force deer to invade fields on farms abutting the hills, to damage fences and hedgerows, and occasionally to cause accidents on narrow lanes.

Issue three: Visitors and access to the Quantock countryside

As we noted in Chapter 7, the growth of tourism in the Quantock region means that its resident population (currently around 29,000) is greatly augmented in summer by visitors. Numbers are hard to come by: they range from Hestercombe with 40,000 visitors per year to Minehead's Butlins with ten times that number. The West Somerset Railway, the region's leading tourist attraction, carries around 210,000 passengers each year. Surveys by the AONB suggest some 400,000 'visit days' on the Quantock Hills each year. Most visits are for only a short time (the average is under two hours) with walks on the upland heaths as the main purpose.[7] Over two-thirds of visits are by 'locals' in the sense of being resident in Somerset; many come at least ten times a year. There is also a widening range of group activity on the hills: orienteering, horse trekking, sponsored walks, and outdoor training for military groups or emergency services. Almost all visitors, even if their purpose is walking or off-road cycling, come by motor vehicle so the summer burden (particularly on holidays and weekends) on roads and parking places is intense.

The Quantock Hills have exceptionally good vehicle access. The main ridge is crossed by a wishbone-shaped minor road from Crowcombe to Over Stowey with a branch off to Holford at Deadwoman's Ditch (Fig. 8.5). Parking has been provided by the AONB at three locations along the road so that the elderly or less able-bodied visitor can sense something of the distinctive hilltop landscape. The hills can also be accessed by car at four points from Staple in the north, through Triscombe Stone in the centre to Lydeard Hill and Cothelstone in the south. All these car parks are at 700 to 1,100 feet so that gentle walks to nearby summits are feasible. In the combes, parking is also provided at Holford and Great Wood, at places of special visitor interest (Kilve Pill, Hawkridge reservoir, and Fyne Court), and in some of the villages abutting the hills (Crowcombe and Nether Stowey).

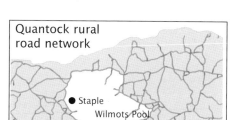

Fig. 8.5 Access by motor vehicle to the Quantock Hills. (Above left) Road network with designated parking areas within the hill country. (Above right) Road sign at Dead Woman's Ditch on the only road to cross east-west across the open moorland area. (Below) Sunday afternoon parking at Crowcombe Park Gate.

One planning problem faced by the AONB is to reduce the visitor pressure on the fragile 'honeypot' heathland areas by introducing visitors to other Quantock landscapes skirting the hills. A 'Quantock Greenway' project was launched in 2001 as an alternative with waymarked routes taking walkers through the skirting villages with their pubs, tea rooms, shops and historical buildings. The Greenway is 36 miles in length and is divided into five segments each representing a few hours walk. The AONB hope that 'the energetic walker could tackle the whole route over two or three days with B&B stops overnight'.

For the walker with literary interests there is also the 'Coleridge Way' launched in 2006. This retraces the footsteps of the romantic poet Samuel Taylor Coleridge (see Chapter 1) along a 36 mile route from his Nether Stowey cottage to the Exmoor village of Porlock. The route follows paths and bridleways through the

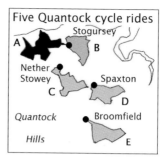

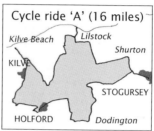

Fig. 8.6 Example of designated cycling routes in and around the Quantock Hills. (Left) Cover of leaflet produced by Sedgemoor District Council. (Upper right) The five recommended routes in the area east of the main ridge of the Quantock Hills. (Lower right) The 16-mile route of Itinerary 'A' called 'Brandy kegs and glatting' circuit taking in coastal stops at Kilve Beach and Lilstock harbour. Source: Redrawn from Bright & Filler, 2000 (note 8).

villages of Holford, Bicknoller and Monksilver and on into Exmoor National Park. Short diversions from the main route take the walker to the Bell Inn at Watchet where he was thought to have started his famous 'Rime of the Ancient Mariner' and to the isolated farmhouse where he wrote 'Kubla Khan'.

For cyclists through the Quantock countryside a series of rides has been put forward by one local authority (Sedgemoor) as part of the National Cycle Network programme.[8] As Fig. 8.6 shows these consist of five circular routes each of between eleven and sixteen miles in length depending on the toughness of the terrain to be tackled. Each ride is built around a theme based on places of interest and stopping points (including village pubs) of interest: (1) the 'Temple of Harmony and the Abode of Love' ride based on Bridgwater ; (2) the 'Ding-dong Bell and the French Connection' ride based on Cannington; (3) the 'The Ancient Mariner and Drake's Drum' ride based on Nether Stowey; (4) the 'Thunder and Lighting Man and Bampfylde Restored' ride based on Broomfield; and (5) the 'Brandy Kegs and Glatting' ride based on Stogursey.

Issue four: The Quantock parish church

We noted in Chapter 7 the problems faced by the smaller Quantock villages in the second half of the last century. Like a medical syndrome, they faced an inter-linked set of losses with the village shop and school, the local pub and garage,

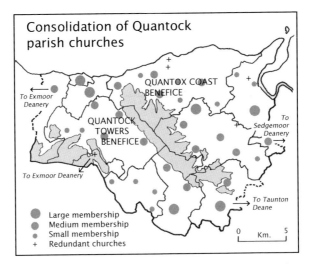

Fig. 8.7 Church reorganization in a period of declining support. The map shows the consolidation of Anglican parish churches into multi-parish groups. Churches which are redundant or already closed are shown. Source: Drawn from data in Davey, 2007 (note 9)

and public transport all linked into a downward spiral. Small villages like Aisholt, Broomfield, and Dodington in the Quantocks and Combe Florey, Elworthy and Tolland in the west illustrate this process. One of the clearest examples of this winnowing has come in the problems faced by the Anglican church. The traditional Victorian pattern of Trollope's Barchester novels in which each parish had its church and each church its resident vicar, rector or curate has long gone.

The Quantock parishes all fall within the Taunton archdeaconry of the diocese of Bath and Wells. As Fig. 8.7 shows, only two of the 33 churches (Watchet and Williton) still have their own priests in the traditional one-to-one pattern.[9] Most parishes are now part of a group, typified by the 'Quantock Towers' group in the west (six churches with a single priest) or the oddly-labelled 'Quantox Coast' group in the north (eight churches under a priest and two assistant priests). Altogether only ten priests and four assistant priests serve all Quantock parishes and a heavy burden now falls on both the heavily-stretched clergy and on lay readers to maintain a continuity of worship. On a historical note, it is important to stress that sharing of clergy between parishes is not a new phenomenon: William Holland, vicar of Over Stowey for forty years from 1779 records in his famous diary several visits to preach at Aisholt.[10]

An ever greater burden of maintaining the church fabric falls on the small congregations that attend services in the parish churches. For the whole of the Quantock parishes, a 2008 survey showed a total membership of 1,160, an average of around thirty for each church. This gives a skewed picture since a few churches were strongly supported, viz. Cannington (113), Williton (104), Nether Stowey (96), Watchet (85) and Bishops Lydeard (76). Over half the churches have twenty or fewer members and in two cases (Dodington and East Quantoxhead) the numbers are under ten. Church membership is not the same as support for many churches overflow at Christmas, Easter and Harvest festival and a once-off crisis in church repair often brings unexpectedly good support from within and outside the parish. Remote churches such as that at Aisholt, are also highly valued by visitors, not least those from the United States and old Commonwealth countries.

Trends in both church membership and support are running against a tide of rising costs born by these beautiful and historically crucial buildings. As Fig. 8.8 shows already five parish churches have closed (Charlinch, Elworthy, Kilton, Lilstock and Otterhampton) and sadly, more may follow. But by what criteria should we save such churches? Their role and importance to the local community might give one set of answers, their wider role in architectural history another. Six of the Quantock churches figure in such informal guides as Simon Jenkins' influential *England's Thousand Best Churches* (1999): Bishops Lydeard, Crowcombe, Goathurst, Kingston St Mary, Stogumber and Stogursey.[11] Robert Dunning also includes Kingston St Mary and Stogursey in his *Fifty Somerset Churches* (1996). His colleague Robin Bush in his parish-by-parish guide to *Somerset* (1994) follows the Michelin precedent and awards stars to twelve Quantock churches. There is enough overlap in the list to suggest a hierarchy could be developed with arguably Stogursey at the crown earning its place as

Fig. 8.8 A number of the smaller Quantock churches are no longer in regular use. The parish church of St Martin of Tours at Elworthy was declared redundant in 1979 but is open for prayer and well maintained by the Redundant Churches Preservation Trust. (Inset) Map of redundant churches.

what Berta Lawrence once called the 'cathedral of the Quantocks'. But my heart goes out to the tiny and remote churches at Aisholt or Elworthy as ones I would love my great-great grandchildren still to be able to visit.

Issue five: Nuclear power and its alternatives

We have already noted in Chapter 7, the arrival on the Quantock coastline of two massive nuclear-power plants at Hinkley Point. In 2008 it was announced by Electricité de France (EDF) the new owners of Hinkley Point B that a third nuclear reactor is planned for Hinkley Point.[12] It is to be a twin unit pressurized reactor, designed to join Hinkley A (Magnox which is now closed and being decommissioned) and Hinkley Point B (AGR) which is due to close in 2016. At the time of writing the government has announced its support in principle and EDF have begun site preparation work. Like its predecessors, the planning application has triggered a hot debate but I focus here on the likely impact on the Quantock region (should it be built) rather than the well-rehearsed arguments for and against nuclear power.

The location of Hinkley C will be adjacent to the present site but on its western side; land has already been acquired. The site includes a seaward section for a temporary jetty and for tunnels for the seawater used for cooling. The prime reason for locating the new station there is closeness to A and B (with their power distribution grids), access to cooling water from Bridgwater Bay, and a location above flood-risks in an area outside an AONB or SSSI.

At the time of writing, argument is raging over the local impact of the five-year construction phase (Fig. 8.9). Construction materials are planned to come in both by the on-site jetty and via an upgraded port at Combwich. At its peak, construction will involve the daily movement of 2,400 workers into Hinkley.

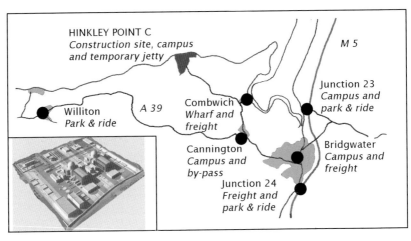

Fig. 8.9 Likely regional impact of construction work for the proposed Hinkley C nuclear power station. Source: EDF Energy, 2010 (note 12).

Accommodation, much of it in temporary campuses, is planned at locations both on and off site with commuting by shuttle busses from park-and-ride sites. Some local organizations have called for new bridges from the M5 at Dunball (Junction 23) over the River Parrett and for a major bypass from Junction 24 to the west of Bridgwater. But what is on current offer from EDF is more modest, a bypass north of Cannington to divert construction traffic from the centre of the village. The debate continues.

A generation of new nuclear stations is unlikely to plug the rising demand for electric power, and other sources are being sought. With the concern over global warming and the search for alternative 'green' sources of power, the potential of the Severn is being looked at once again and this has implications for the Quantock region. Tidal mills are mentioned in the Somerset Domesday and given the Bristol Channel's huge tidal range (up to a 50 feet maximum, second only to Canada's Bay of Fundy), it is not surprising that plans for major tidal power schemes have come and gone since 1850. A stone in St Decuman's churchyard at Watchet commemorates Osborne Reynolds, one of its pioneer engineers. In October 2007 the government's Sustainable Development Commission (CDC) published the latest report entitled *Turning the Tide* on the potential of tidal power in the UK.[13] Among the ten schemes it reviewed for the Severn, one of them – the Bridgwater Bay tidal lagoon – was shortlisted as worth further evaluation. As shown in Fig. 8.10, the scheme envisaged a twelve-mile long concrete barrier running in an arc north-east from Hinkney Point to Brean Down. As proposed, it would impound over twenty square miles of the present bay. Turbines set in the barrier would generate some 2.6 Twh of power per year.

Like nuclear power, tidal power has both strong advocates and detractors. On the positive side, the Bridgwater Bay scheme would have a long life (120 years

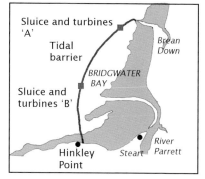

Fig. 8.10 Tidal power. (Left) One of the many tidal schemes proposed for the Severn estuary over the last 150 years: the proposed Bridgwater Bay tidal barrage, 2010. (Right) An evocation of tidal power in the 'Ebb and Flow' structure on the river bank south of Combwich. Source: Severn Tidal Power Feasibility Study, 2010 (note 13).

minimum) and supply a local and green energy source. It would provide flood protection for coastal communities, notably Burnham on Sea, and provide so called 'leisure friendly' waters within the barrier for recreational users. Construction would provide a short-term boost to the local economy and a long-term increase in tourism. On the negative side, there would be a loss of inter-tidal habitats from the Bridgwater Bay reserve and impede fish migration. Accelerated silting in some areas and erosion in others is likely. Unless expensive locks were included in the scheme, the remaining use of the Parrett for shipping would also stop. Reclaiming land within the bay on a Dutch 'polders' model is more neutral. The scheme, like so many previous tidal plans, remains on the drawing board and the proposal has been shelved for further review after 2015. Yet another tidal scheme kicked into the long grass.

To judge from a benchend in Bishops Lydeard church (Fig, 8.11), wind power in the Quantocks goes back to at least the 1550s as a useful if minor energy source. The best locations for modern turbines would be, in purely engineering terms, the high-ridge of the Quantock Hills, its south-west face ideally placed across the dominant wind direction. Unlike the pylon-clad Tehachapi Hills in southern California, this nightmare-like prospect for the Quantock Hills is not

Fig. 8.11 Wind power has deep roots in the Quantocks. A sixteenth-century benchend in Bishops Lydeard parish church (see Plate 8B) showing a wind mill and miller.

on any agenda I know. But, as this book goes to press, the decision by Somerset County Council to sell off 2,000 acres of woods and moorland (Great Wood, Customs Common and Thorncombe Hill) reinforces the need for bodies such as the AONB and Friends of Quantock to be constantly vigilant if the biodiversity and public access of the area is to continue to be protected. Our grandchildren and their successors will always have critical landscape problems to face.

THE QUANTOCK POETS: A FINAL WALK

The Yosemite Valley in California became one of America's first National Parks in 1890. A year earlier the naturalist John Muir gave a lecture with lantern slides extolling its beauty to a San Francisco audience. At its end, a lady in the audience asked Muir which place in the Yosemite he would visit 'if he only had a few hours'. After some thought Muir replied: 'Madam, I should sit down and weep'.

If faced with a problem similar to Muir, where in the Quantocks would I go to spend a last few hours? To the north, to see 'Kilve's delightful shore'? To the east, to see again the exquisite Georgian house at Barford Park or walk in the Spring through the fritillaries in Fairfield's garden? To the south, to Hestercombe with its triple bonus of three great gardens of different ages all in one spot? To the west, to ponder life's deep mysteries, in the great Cistercian abbey at Cleeve?

After much head scratching, I defer to the judgment of Coleridge and the Wordsworths and decide to walk on a circuit from Holford (see map in Fig. 8.12).[14] Dorothy described the countryside here in unforgettable terms:

Wherever we turn we have woods, smooth downs, and valleys with small brooks running down through meadows hardly ever intersected with hedgerows but scattered over with trees. The hills that cradle these villages are either covered with fern or bilberries or oakwoods – walks extend for miles over the hilltops, the great beauty of which is their wild simplicity.

So I set off. Leaving the car by the oddly named Bowling Green at Holford (**1**) the walk takes me up Hodder's Combe passing the octagonal house and the steep woods of Willougby Cleeve on the right. On, past the spot where we used as boys to camp by the stream (**2**) and where – running low on funds after honeymooning at Combe Lodge: see Fig. 6.4 – we gained permission from the Fairfield estate office again and completed our first week of married life under canvas. Now, as then, the slots of red deer can be seen in the streamside mud. Forking right, leaving Somerton Combe to the left, it's puffing up the gentle pull through the oakwoods of Lady's Edge and out of the wooded combe onto the open heathland and checking the map at Bicknoller Post (**3**) (see Plate 16D).

From there, views north to Beacon Hill and west towards Dunster and Minehead open up.

Then south along the old Saxon trunk road along Black Ball Hill to Halsway Post with the distinctive sound of a West Somerset Railway steam locomotive pulling up the slope to Crowcombe Heathfield (Fig.6.6) and distant views of the folly on Willett Hill (Plate 12B) close to the edge of the Exmoor National Park. Then east to the head of Frog Combe (**4**) (Plate 2A) and across the head of Lady Combe to push through the oak scrub towards the bank of the Iron Age

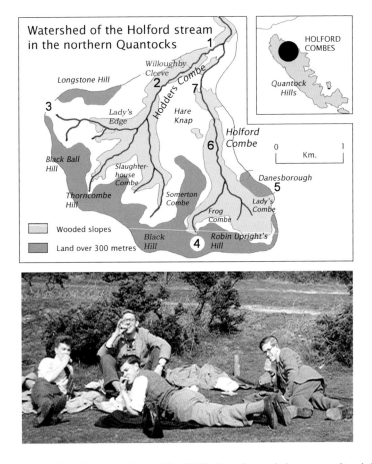

Fig. 8.12 A final walk. (Above) *Map of the Holford combes and the surrounding hills to show numbered features on the walking route followed in the text.* (Below) *Because family finances didn't run to a camera, there are few very early snaps from this area in my records. The one shown dates from June 1949 and records a lunch stop on a celebratory 'post-exams' Quantock walk. Author is nearest camera with three fellow sixth-formers from Dr Morgan's (left to right, Ivor Slocombe, Alan Warren and John Griffiths); all four of us went on to study at Cambridge. Typical for that formal pre-anorak period, we all wore ties and tweed jackets and carried our substantial lunch in rexine shopping bags rather than rucksacks. Photo by Gordon Palmer.*

fort on Danesborough (**5**) (Fig. 3.5). From its northern lip, a three-quarter circle of countryside opens up. North is the silver gleam of Severn and the Welsh coast with the Black Mountains visible on a good day. Below the ridge of Hare Knap and beyond it Longstone Hill with the memorial block of conifers to mourn for Holford's war losses, a view beautifully captured by the Somerset artist Jenny Graham in her 'Toward Wales' painting which hangs in our Chew Magna home.[15] To the northwest is the distant ridge of the Mendips, Brent Knoll in the middle distance, and nearer the low hill of my family home at Pawlett with the great meander sweeps of the Parrett between. The church spire at Stringston and the group of woodlots around Fairfield occupy the nearest lowlands. On the coast, a feature new since my boyhood walks, the blocks of Hinkley Point power station look like counters on a Monopoly board. Then, reluctantly, down along the open ridge of Woodlands Hill past a herd of grazing ponies and sharp left down a steep valley-side trail (dodging a sleeping adder) to meet Holford Combe at the ford (**6**).

This is my first Quantock memory: a family picnic on a warm Sunday afternoon (after morning chapel), building dams across the stream with my two brothers and imagining we lived in an Arthur Ransome world.[16] It was an idyllic activity which I tried to pass on to my own children, and hopefully they to theirs. Then a leisurely stop at Combe House (**7**) for a cream tea in the garden and the last half-mile down the combe past the old post office to find the car. I suppose the whole circuit might have been seven or so miles in length; an enjoyable two-hour trot as a fit teenager but now ever longer and more testing as the years go by. Maybe now four hours or more. But as Dorothy Wordsworth might agree (her brother was, I fancy, more a Lakeland man), as good a four hours as life has to offer. Go to the Quantocks and try the walk yourself: you will then know why I wrote this book.

Appendix

HINTS FOR A QUANTOCK VISITOR

One of our family's favourite radio programmes is *Desert Island Discs*, and we've often thought – I expect like you – which eight gramophone records we might take away to a desert island. Following the same principles, I've made here eight Quantock selections (for walks, parish churches, other buildings to visit, and books to read). All are highly personal choices and I invite you to cross-out mine and replace with your own. Numbers in brackets give the National Grid reference for each location.

Eight Quantock walks

Although there are many books of walks in Quantock country, I suggest your best investment is the two Ordnance Survey maps covering the area at a useful 1:25,000 Explorer scale (Sheet 140: 'Quantock Hills and Bridgwater' and Sheet OL9 'Exmoor'). These clearly show footpaths, parking places and some inns. Since most visitors come to the area by car I begin each of the walks at a car park: four in the hill country and four in the lowlands. Rather than giving a detailed itinerary I simply suggest some general directions and leave the precise route and map reading to you.

In the hill country, there are excellent car parks at both low and high levels which provide a launching base for hill and combe walks. Walks from the car park at *[1] Holford Bowling Green* (154~411) can range from a brief stroll up and back Hodders Combe (two miles or so) to a more testing circuits combining combes and hills in longer circuits (see that described at the end of Chapter 8). The Forestry Commission at *[2] Great Wood* (176~369) suggests several forest walks and provides a large glade for children to let off steam. High-elevation car parks are located from Cothelstone in the south to Staple in the north. That at *[3] Triscombe Stone* (164~360) gives an opportunity to walk up to the Quantock's highest point at Wills Neck or amble north along the line of beeches to Crowcombe Park Gate. Equally *[4] Staple Plantation* (117~411) allows circuits to Beacon Hill, the Great Road across to Holford, and Weacombe.

In the lowlands, *[5] Kilve Beach* (144~443) offers an attractive 'quadrilateral walk': west along the coast path, inland and south to East Quantoxhead (Court House and church), east to Kilve church (leaving East Wood to your right), then tea at the Chantry, and back north to the car. By heading east towards Lilstock some fine cliff scenery and the remains of the old port can be seen. From *[6] Watchet Harbour* (071~435) it is worth following the old mineral railway line south towards Washford and Cleeve Abbey. Another coastal walk is from *[7] Steart* (275~459) east along the beach to the bird observation tower. This gives splendid views of the mud-flats and Bridgwater Bay reserve and looks west towards the Quantocks. Finally, I'd recommend a village walk: *[8] Stogumber* (098~373) is well worth exploring. Leave your car in the village square by St Mary's church and the 'White Horse' pub and try each of the roads radiating out. If you're lucky enough to be there on a June weekend when (for the last thirty years) a score of gardens are open and there is lunch at the Village Hall, all the better.

Eight Quantock parish churches

The Quantock's medieval parish churches are amongst the finest in England and I make no apology for giving them here as a separate category. With over thirty fine parish churches to choose from, most of them open, you should never be at a loss and I've fought to keep the number down to eight. But among my favourites are *[1] St Andrew, Stogursey* (205~428), perhaps the finest of the Quantock churches (Berta Lawrence called it the Quantock's 'cathedral') with its great Norman arches and Verney chapel. The church of the *[2] Holy Ghost, Crowcombe* (141~367) was described by Simon Jenkins in his *England's Thousand Best Churches* as a 'place of bliss'. It has among the best Quantock benchends, a neighbouring Church House, and stands at the entrance to Crowcombe Court.

Many churches have fine stone carvings and *[3] St Edward, Goathurst* (256~343) with its memorial Tynte chapel and *[4] St Peter and Paul, Combe Florey* (151~312) with Sir John de Meriet and his two wives are both worth visiting for these alone. *[5] St Mary, Bishops Lydeard* (168~298) with its tall red tower and colourful bench ends and *[6] St George, Bicknoller* (111~394) with its churchyard memorials must also get a mention. I'm conscious how many fine churches I've ignored but include my last two churches not for their great architecture but simply as small and remote places of worship over the centuries: *[7] All Saints, Aisholt* (194~357) and the now redundant but still open *[8] St Martins, Elworthy* (083~350) are well worth tracking down.

Eight other Quantock buildings

Two unmissable places which are open year round are *[1] Hestercombe* (242~288) in the south of the Quantocks and *[2] Cleeve Abbey* (047~407) in the far west. The first has three gardens of historical interest illustrating eighteenth-century,

Victorian and Edwardian approaches to garden design. Cleeve retains a remarkably complete set of monastic buildings from the Cistercian foundation. Both are 'children friendly'. The gardens at *[3] Fairfield* (188~430) are open twice each Spring and the Elizabethan house itself over the summer months in aid of Stogursey Church. No visit to the Quantocks should miss the coastal port of Watchet: its *[4] Harbour and Town Museum* (071~435) gives an insights into many aspects of the settlement's history.

Two places in the east and west are *[5] Cannington Walled Garden* (258~396) built next to the old nunnery and with glasshouses and a welcome café and *[6] Crowcombe Heathfield Station* (137~ 343). The latter is an iconic halt on the West Somerset Railway (do take a train ride) and much loved by film-makers. Finally, the two National Trust properties. *[7] Fyne Court* (223~371) at Broomfield is also headquarters for the Quantock Hills AONB and has lots of information about the area. *[8] Coleridge's Cottage* (191~399) at Nether Stowey catches the spirit of the great but troubled poet; the cottage was the hearth for much of his finest verse and the rear garden has been restored.

Eight Quantock books

My favourite book about the Quantocks remains *[1]* Berta Lawrence's *Quantock Country* (Westaway, 1952), now sixty years old but still one of the best guides. If you can still find a copy, then *[2]* Vincent Waite's *Portrait of the Quantocks* (Robert Hale, 1964) is not far behind. Our understanding of Quantock prehistory has been transformed by *[3]* Hazel Riley's beautifully illustrated survey of its archaeology, *The Historic Landscape of the Quantock Hills* (English Heritage, 2006). *[4]* Tom Mayberry in his *Coleridge and Wordsworth in the West Country* (Sutton, 1992) skilfully recreates the atmosphere of the *annus mirabilis*. A different view of the Quantocks at that time is given in *[5]* the diary of William Holland, a Quantock parson from 1799-1818, has been edited as *Paupers and Pig Killers* (Sutton, 1984).

At the millennium, many Quantock parishes published guides to their villages and I've chosen *[6] Cannington Reflections* (2000) as it catches the spirit of the place so well. Look for such local books in any one of the villages in which you stay. Old pictures of the Quantocks have been patiently gathered together by Audrey Mead and David Worthy in three volumes: *[7] Quantock Miscellany* (Frian Press, 2006) and its companions are a delight. Finally, a reference work. The Quantock region will eventually be covered by three volumes of the Victoria County History of Somerset and two have so far been published. *[8]* Robert Dunning's *Volume 5: Williton and Freemanors Hundred* (Oxford University Press, 1985) is a scholar's delight which will keep you interested on many a fireside winter evening. Of the books mentioned above, some are still in print, others may be found in local second-hand bookshops (or, more dully, through the internet). All are borrowable from local libraries.

Other Quantocks 'eights'

I resisted the temptation to add sections on 'eight Quantock inns', 'eight B&Bs', 'eight rentable cottages', etc. since some of these tend to change rapidly. Suffice to say that there are many memorable taverns, a score of welcoming farmhouses or converted mills to stay in, and plenty of places to rent. Searching the web and contacting local tourist centres (at Bridgwater, Taunton and Williton) will provide up-to-date information. Do go and stay, especially at times like late September when so many Quantock artists will have open studios illustrating their work. The National Trust and the AONB both have offices at Fyne Court and these have excellent information about the area.

There are an ever-increasing number of web sites on the Quantock Hills and the surrounding region. Most valuable is the Quantock Hills AONB website *(www.quantockhills.com)* which is regularly updated and is a mine of information about the hills and their management. Also useful is the news from surrounding villages as given in the Quantock Community Newsletter *(www.quantockonline.co.uk)* and in the Friends of Quantocks Newsletter *(www.friendsofquantock.com)*. For those visiting or staying in the Quantocks the Somerset site *(www.visitsomerset.co.uk)* with links to local tourist offices is invaluable. Many farms and places to stay or to visit have their own sites. Those interested in individual historical places within the Quantocks, will find the Somerset Environment Historical Record website *(www.somerset.gov.uk/HER)* a definitive source.

End Notes

Preface: A Remembered Earth
[1] N. Scott Momaday, *The Way to Rainy Mountain* (Albuquerque: University of New Mexico Press, 1969), 83.
[2] Peter Haggett, *Agriculture and Land Use in the Quantock Parishes, West Somerset* (Cambridge: Geographical Tripos, Part I, 1953).
[3] Berta Lawrence, *Quantock Country* (London: Westaway, 1952); H. C. Darby (ed.), *An Historical Geography of England before A. D. 1800* (Cambridge: Cambridge University Press, 1951).
[4] See James Crowden, *Literary Somerset* (Chard: Flagon Press, 2010), 127-128.

One. *Prelude*: A Quantock Tapestry
[1] Freya Stark, *Traveller's Prelude* (London: John Murray, 1950), 16.
[2] W. H. P. Greswell, *The Land of Quantock: A Descriptive and Historical Account* (Taunton: Barnicott and Pearce, 1903); Berta Lawrence, *Quantock Country* (London: Westaway, 1952), 14; William Luke Nichols, *The Quantocks and Their Associations,* 2nd edn., (London: Sampson Low, Marston and Co, 1891).
[3] Sedgemoor District Council, *Sedgemoor Landscape Assessment and Countryside Design Summary* (Bridgwater, 2003).
[4] The boundaries are discussed in W. J. Taylor, 'Should Exmoor be extended?', *Exmoor Review*, **14** (1973), 63-66 and Brian Pearce, '50 years ago: the battle for Exmoor National Park', *Exmoor Review*, **45** (2004), 68-71.
[5] Lawrence, 1952 (note 2), 14.
[6] Nichols, 1891 (note 2), 1; Maxwell Fraser, *Somerset* (London: Great Western Railway, 1934), 29.
[7] From Wordsworth's *Prelude*. This was an autobiographical poem first written in 1798 (when he was 28) and reworked over the rest of his life. It was not published until after his death in 1850 when the title was given to it by his widow, Mary.
[8] There have been literally scores of volumes written on the Coleridge-Wordsworth partnership. The three I have found most useful are Berta Lawrence, *Coleridge and Wordsworth in Somerset* (Newton Abbot: David and Charles, 1970); Tom Mayberry, *Coleridge and Wordsworth: The Crucible of Friendship* (Stroud: Sutton, 2000); and Reggie Watters, *Samuel Taylor Coleridge: The West Country Years* (Nether Stowey: Friends of Coleridge, 2003). The Mayberry volume contains a transcript of Dorothy Wordsworth's Alfoxden Journal on pp. 158-164. The delightful line drawings are by Edmund Hort New from W. A. Knight, *Coleridge and Wordsworth in the West Country: Their Friendship, Work and Surroundings* (New York: Charles Scribner, 1914). Useful guides to sites and walks associated with the two poets are provided in R. Watters and D. Woolf, *Walking with Coleridge in the Quantocks* (Nether Stowey: Coleridge Cottage, 1992) and R. Evans, *Somerset in the Footsteps of Coleridge and Wordsworth* (Bridgwater: Author, 2000).
[9] Samuel Taylor Coleridge, pencil and chalk drawing by Robert Hancock, 1796; William Wordsworth, pencil and chalk drawing by Robert Hancock, 1798 (National Portrait Gallery.
[10] E. de Selincourt, *The Early Letters of William and Dorothy Wordsworth (1787-1805)* (Oxford: Clarendon Press, 1935).
[11] Ruth Tongue, *Somerset Folklore* (London: The Folklore Society, 1965), 187 and Berta Lawrence, *Somerset Legends* (Newton Abbot: David and Charles, 1973).
[12] A. W. Smith, 'And did those feet...?: the legend of Christ's visit to Britain', *Folklore*, **100** (1989), 63-83.
[13] A useful summary of the legends of the area is given in Jennifer Westwood and Jacqueline Simpson, *The Lore of the Land: A Guide to England's Legends* (London: Penguin, 2005), 634-657.
[14] P. P. Wright, *The Rural Benchends of Somerset* (Amersham: Avebury, 1983).

[15] Robin Bush, *Somerset: The Complete Guide* (Wimborne: Dovecote Press, 1994), 35-36.

[16] Bush, 1994 (note 15), 46-47, 70, 188-189. A useful guide to Crosse is provided by Audrey Mead, *Andrew Crosse: Scientific Squire of Broomfield* (Fyne Court: Somerset Trust for Nature Conservation, 2000).

[17] A useful summary of these local links is provided by James Crowden, *Literary Somerset* (Winsham: Flagon Press, 2010). This covers the centuries of Somerset writing from St Gildas the Wise (516-570) who lived on Steep Holm up to the present.

[18] Parson Holland 'took quiet possession' of the Vicarage and Parish Church of Over Stowey on September 3rd, 1779. About half his diaries survive and have been edited by Jack Ayres (ed.), *Paupers and Pig Killers: The Diary of William Holland, A Somerset Parson, 1799-1818* (Stroud: Sutton, 1984). As a child, the novelist Phyllis Bottome lived in the same vicarage a century later before moving to the United States, see her memories of Quantock village life in *Search for a Soul* (New York: Reynal & Hitchcock, 1948); quotation, 21-22.

[19] J. T. Banks (ed.), *Congenial Spirits: The Selected Letters of Virginia Woolf* (London: Hogarth Press, 1989).

[20] This is based on my Jean Rees Memorial Lecture, 'A Quantock Light' given to the Chandos Society of Artists at the Bridgwater Arts Centre in March 2011. On the Halsway school see R.M.Billingham, 'A Somerset draw for painters. Victorian artists at Halsway Manor'. *Country Life,* (August 1977), 428-30 and H. Alexander, 'John William North ARA RWS', *The Old Water-colour Society's Club,* **5** (1928), 35-48.

[21] F. Howes, 'Cecil (James) Sharp, 1859-1924', in S. Sadie (ed.), *The New Grove Dictionary of Music and Musicians,* **23** (2001), 219-220. Peter Lewis, 'Somerset folk songs: Cecil Sharp's visits to the Quantocks', *Friends of Quantock, Newsletter,* **66** (Autumn 2009), 3-4.

[22] For the origins of Quantock names I've relied heavily on E. Ekwall, *The Concise Oxford Dictionary of English Place-Names,* 4th edn., (Oxford: Oxford University Press, 1960) and Victor Watts, *The Cambridge Dictionary of English Place Names.* (Cambridge: Cambridge University Press, 2004). See also the discussion of 'Quantock' in Mary Siraut, Robert Dunning and Ken Brown, *The Quantocks: A Past Worth Preserving* (Tiverton: Somerset Books, 1992), 7.

[23] T. Chubb, *A Descriptive List of the Printed Maps of Somersetshire, 1575-1914* (Taunton: Somerset Archaeological and Natural History Society, 1914). Keith Needell, *Printed Maps of Somersetshire, 1575-1860,* 2nd. edn. (Muswell Hill: Privately printed, 1995).

[24] Description of the 1609 Quantock map for Earl of Northumberland in Siraut *et al,* 1992 (note 22), 10-12.

[25] Nichols, 1891 (note 2); Greswell, 1902 (note 2); B. F. Cresswell, *The Quantock Hills: Their Combes and Villages* (Taunton:. Bamicott and Pearce, 1904); W. H. P. Greswell, *Dumnonia and the Valley of the Parrett. A Historical Perspective* (Taunton: Barnicott and Pearce, 1922). E. H. Smith, *Quantock Life and Rambles* (Taunton: Barnicotts, 1939).

[26] Lawrence, 1952 (note 2) and Vincent Waite, *Portrait of the Quantocks* (London: Robert Hale, 1964).

[27] W. A. E.Ussher, *The Geology of the Quantock Hills: Memoirs of the Geological Survey, Sheet 295* (London: HMSO, 1908). Hazel Riley, *The Historic Landscape of the Quantock Hills* (Swindon: English Heritage, 2006).

[28] Much of the archival material for the Quantocks is necessarily parish based; see J. E. King, *Inventory of Parochial Documents in the Diocese of Bath and Wells in the County of Somerset* (Taunton: Somerset County Council, 1938) and the updated catalogues at the Somerset Heritage Centre, Taunton. The key volume reviewing the role the parish is N. J. G. Pounds, *A History of the English Parish* (Cambridge: Cambridge University Press, 2000).

[29] The western and eastern parishes of the Quantocks are covered in two fine volumes: R. W. Dunning, (ed.), *Victoria History of the County of Somerset, V*ol. *5: Williton and Freemanors Hundred* (Oxford: Oxford University Press, 1992) and *Vol. 6 : Bridgwater and Neighbouring Parishes* (Oxford: Oxford University Press, 1985). The southern Quantock parishes in Taunton Deane have yet to be published.

[30] The distinctive geographical areas which abut the Quantocks have been well documented, see Michael Williams, *The Draining of the Somerset Levels* (Cambridge: Cambridge University Press, 1970); Tom Mayberry, *The Vale of Taunton Past* (Chichester: Phillimore, 1998); and Ian Mercer and Brian Pearce, *Exmoor: National Park Guide* (Dulverton: Exmoor National Park, 2001). The history of the three bordering towns is treated in J. F. and J. C. Lawrence, *A History of Bridgwater* (Chichester: Phillimore, 2005); Mayberry, 1998 (above); and Hilary Binding and D. J. Stevens, *Minehead: A New History* (Minehead: Exmoor Press, 1977).

[31] Maps of the ecclesiastical parishes for all counties is given in C. R. Humphery-Smith, *The Phillimore Atlas and Index of Parish Registers* (Chichester: Phillimore, 1984).

[32] This is not the place to go into the theology of regions and their identification. I've probably written at too much length on this already in P. Haggett, *Geography: A Global Synthesis* (London: Pearson, 2001), chapter 12 ('The web of regions'); and in *The Geographer's Art.* (Oxford: Blackwells, 1990), chapter 4 ('Regional synthesis').

Two. The Lie of the Land

[1] Vincent Waite, *Portrait of the Quantocks* (London: Robert Hale, 1964), 16.

[2] The foundations of understanding Quantock geology were laid down by Henry de la Beche in his *Report on the Geology of Cornwall, Devon and West Somerset* (Memoirs of the Geological Survey of Great Britain, 1839). A modern view of the geology of the area is provided in P. Hardy, *The Geology of Somerset* (Bradford-on-Avon: Ex Libris Press, 1999). I have drawn heavily in this chapter on my essay in the R.J.Chorley memorial volume, see P. Haggett, 'On the landform history of Chorley's West Somerset', in David R. Stoddart (ed.), *Process and Form in Geomorphology* (London: Routledge, 1997), 215-242: Richard Chorley was a Minehead boy who went on to be Professor of Physical Geography at Cambridge. Excellent guides to local Quantock areas are given in Eric Robinson, *The Geology of Watchet and its Neighbourhood, Somerset* (Geologists Association Guide, **66**, 2006) and Hugh Prudden, *Geology and Landscape of Taunton Deane* (Taunton: Taunton Deane Borough Council, 2001).

[3] The key early monographs for the geology of the Quantocks is in W. A. E. Ussher, *The Geology of the Quantock Hills:, Memoir of the Geological Survey, Sheet 295* (London: HMSO, 1908). This was revised eighty years later by E. A. Edmonds and B. J. Williams, *Geology of the Country around Taunton and the Quantock Hills: Memoir for 1 :50 000 Geological Sheet 295, NS.* (London: HMSO, 1985).

[4] This is also known as the Hercynian or Armorican mountain-building phase.

[5] W. G. V. Balchin, 'The erosion surfaces of Exmoor and adjacent areas', *Geographical Journal*, **68** (1952), 453-476.

[6] S. Campbell, *et al*, *Quaternary of South West England* (London: Chapman and Hall, 1998).

[7] E. C. Penning-Rowsell, 'Historical changes in river patterns near Holford, Somerset', *Somerset Archaeological and Natural History Society, Proceedings*, **118** (1974), 39-43.

[8] L. F. Curtis, *Soils of Exmoor Forest*, Soil Survey Special Publication, **5** (Harpenden: Soil Survey of England and Wales, 1971).

[9] J. B. Harley and R. W. Dunning, *Somerset Maps: Day and Masters 1782, Greenwood, 1822* (Taunton Castle: Somerset Record Society, 1981).

[10] C. Kidson, 'The shingle complexes of Bridgwater Bay'. *Institute of British Geographers, Transactions*, **28** (1960), 75-87; C. Kidson and A. P. Carr, 'Beach drift experiments at Bridgwater Bay, Somerset', *Proceedings of the Bristol Naturalists Society*, **30** (1961), 163-180. For a general review of the coastline of this part of Somerset see J. A. Steers, *The Coastline of England and Wales*, 2nd. edn. (Cambridge: Cambridge University Press, 1964).

[11] Edmonds & Williams, 1985 (note 3), 3.

[12] See discussion in Haggett, 1997 (note 2).

[13] A general introduction to the building stone of the region is given in N. Pevsner, *The Buildings of England: South and West Somerset* (Harmondsworth: Penguin, 1958), 13-15. See also the useful review by Hugh Prudden, 'Somerset building stone: a guide', *Somerset Archaeological and Natural History Society, Proceedings*, **146** (2002), 27-36.

[14] C. M. Gerrard, 'Ham Hill stone: a medieval distribution pattern from Somerset', *Oxford Journal of Archaeology*, **4** (1985), 105-116.

[15] J. R. Hamilton and J. F. Lawrence, *Men and Mining on the Quantocks*, 2nd. ed. (Exmoor Mines Research Group, 2008).

[16] For a discussion of limekilns with distribution map see Prudden, 2001 (note 2), 32-34.

[17] University of Bristol Reconstruction Research Group, *Gloucestershire, Somerset and Wiltshire: Land Classification*, (Bristol: University of Bristol, 1947).

Three. Peopling the Landscape

[1] L. V. Grinsell, *Prehistoric Sites in the Quantock Country* (Taunton: Somerset Archaeological and Natural History Society, Aspects of Somerset; Archaeology Series, No. 1, 1991).

[2] Hazel Riley, *The Historic Landscape of the Quantock Hills* (Swindon: English Heritage, 2006), Fig. 2.25, p. 43.

[3] Frederick Jackson Turner's ideas were first expounded for me sixty years ago by J. H. Paterson in his outstanding Cambridge lectures on the settlement of the American West. Turner's seminal paper on 'The significance of the frontier in American history' was written in 1893; and developed in F. J. Turner, *The Frontier in American History* (New York: Holt, 1921).

[4] The central archaeological texts which I've drawn on in this chapter to supplement Leslie Grinsell's early work on the Quantocks (note 1) are Hazel Riley's outstanding monograph on the Quantock Hills (note 2) and Michael Aston and Ian Burrow (eds.), *Archaeology of Somerset: A Review to 1500 AD* (Taunton, Somerset County Council, 1982). Detailed descriptions of individual sites are given in Lesley and Roy Adkins, *Field Guide to Somerset Archaeology* (Wimborne: Dovecote Press, 1992) and online through the Somerset Environment Historical Record.

[5] M. Bell, 'Intertidal peats and the archaeology of coastal change in the Severn Estuary, Bristol Channel and Pembrokeshire', *Geological Society, Special Publications*, **175** (2000), 372-392.

[6] The diagram is based on multiple sources including Ian Simmons, *Environmental History of Great Britain* (Edinburgh: Edinburgh University Press, 2001) and the pollen diagrams in H. Vedel and J. Lange, *Trees and Bushes in Wood and Hedgerow* (London: Methuen, 1960), 206-213.

[7] Carl Ortwin Sauer, 'Seashore – Primitive home of man?', in J. Leighley (ed.) *Land and Life: A Selection from the Writings of Carl Ortwin Sauer* (Berkeley: University of California Press, 1963), 300-312.

[8] For accounts of the Palaeolithic in Somerset see the chapters by J. Cook and R. Jacobi in Aston & Burrow, 1982 (note 4) and Riley, 2006 (note 2), 15-18. Many discoveries in the Doniford area are the work of A. L. Wedlake.

[9] For the Mesolithic period see Riley, 2006 (note 2), 18-19 and the chapter by C. Norman in Aston & Burrow, 1982 (note 4), 15-22. The impact of the Mesolithic peoples on the landscape is explored in I. G. Simmons, *The Environmental Impact of Later Mesolithic Cultures: The Creation of Moorland Landscape in England and Wales* (Edinburgh: Edinburgh University Press, 1996). See also his discussion of hunter-gatherers and fisherfolk in I. G. Simmons, *An Environmental History of Britain: From 10,000 Years Ago to the Present* (Edinburgh: Edinburgh University Press, 2001), 23-50.

[10] See Riley, 2006 (note 2), 19-28 and the chapter by S. Minnitt in Aston & Burrow, 1982 (note 4), 23-28.

[11] A. Ellison in Aston & Burrow, 1982 (note 4), 43-52 and Riley, 2006 (note 2), 28-50.

[12] Barry Cunliffe in Aston & Burrow, 1982 (note 4), 53-62; Riley, 2006 (note 2), 51-72; and Ian Burrow, *Hillfort and Hill-top Settlement in Somerset in the First Millennium AD.* (Oxford: Oxford University Press, 1981).

[13] See the detailed description in Adkins & Adkins, 1992 (note 4), 49.

[14] Research on the Roman period is well summarized in P. Leech, *Roman Somerset*,

(Wimborne: Dovecote Press, 2001). For the Quantock Hills see Riley, 2006 (note 2), 72-76.

[15] P. Rahtz in Aston & Burrow, 1982 (note 4), 99-108 and R. Mansell Prothero, 'The Bristol Channel coastlands; early cultural contacts', *Scottish Geographical Magazine*, **65** (1949), 44-54.

[16] References for the Domesday literature on Somerset are given in Chapter 4 (see notes 3 and 5).

[17] The distribution of settlements in Somerset was studied by Beatrice Swainson, herself the daughter of a Quantock vicar. Her M.A. thesis *A Study of Rural Settlement in Somerset* (1932) is lodged in the Somerset Studies Library, Taunton. Summaries of her findings were published as B. M. Swainson, 'Rural settlement in Somerset', *Geography*, **20** (1935), 113-124 and 'Dispersion and agglomeration of rural settlement in Somerset', *Geography*, **29** (1944), 1-8.

[18] A. L. Wedlake, *History of Watchet* (Dulverton: Exmoor Press, 1973) and *Anglo-Saxon Watchet and the Mint* (Watchet: Privately printed, 1985). Tony Scrase, *Somerset Towns: Changing Fortunes 800 -1800* (Stroud: Tempus, 2005), 7-40.

[19] G. B. Grundy, *Saxon Charters and Field Names of Somerset* (Taunton: Somerset Archaeological and Natural History Society, 1935).

[20] I've made use of Margaret Gelling and Ann Cole, *Landscape of Place Names* (Donington: Shaun Tyas, 2003) and W. H. P. Greswell, 'The Quantocks and their place-names', *Somerset Archaeology and Natural History,* **46** (1900), 125-48. Other sources for place name evidence are given in Chapter 1 (note 22).

[21] Like other students, I'm indebted to Michael Costen for a number of studies of Somerset's administrative organization. See his *Origins of Somerset* (Manchester: University Press, 1992) and his chapter 'The making of the shire', in Tom Mayberry and Hilary Binding (eds.), *Somerset: The Millennium Book* (Tiverton: Somerset Books, 1999), 11-22.

[22] N. J. G. Pounds, *A History of the English Parish* (Cambridge: Cambridge University Press, 2000).

[23] P. J. Fowler, *The Farming of Prehistoric Britain* (Cambridge: Cambridge University Press, 1983). See also the discussion in I.G. Simmons, 2001 (note 9), 66-67.

Four. Medieval Modifications

[1] Arthur Moss, *Aisholt and its Church* (Spaxton: Friends of Aisholt Church, 1995); second stanza from poem on p. 8.

[2] Robin Bush, *Somerset: The Complete Guide* (Wimborne: Dovecote Press, 1994), 23.

[3] The translated text for the Somerset Domesday is given in J. H. Round, 'Introduction to the Somerset Domesday', in W. Page (ed.), *Victoria History of the County of Somerset, Vol. 1.* (London: University of London, 1906), 383-433. For an updated version with useful maps of probable Domesday locations see C. Thorn and F. Thorn (eds.), *Domesday Book, Volume 8, Somerset* (Chichester: Phillimore, 1980).

[4] Thorn & Thorn (note 3), 19:7.

[5] R. W. Finn and P. Wheatley, 'Somerset', in H. C. Darby and R. W. Finn (eds.), *The Domesday Geography of South-West England* (Cambridge: Cambridge University Press, 1967), 132-222.

[6] See the discussion by F. W. Morgan, 'Domesday woodland in southwest England', *Antiquity*, **10** (1936), 306-324 and in Finn & Wheatley, 1967 (note 5), 173-179.

[7] Finn & Wheatley, 1967 (note 5), 190-194.

[8] See the discussion in R. W. Dunning, *Somerset Castles* (Tiverton: Somerset Books, 1995). Descriptions of individual castles are given in R. and L. Adkins, *Field Guide to Somerset Archaeology* (Wimborne: Dovecote Press, 1992), 91-92, 105-107 and in Hazel Riley, *The Historic Landscape of the Quantock Hills* (Swindon: English Heritage, 2006), 91-93.

[9] Stogursey is well described in a number of places. See especially the definitive account in R. W. Dunning, (ed.), *Victoria History of the County of Somerset, Vol. 6 : Bridgwater and Neighbouring Parishes* (Oxford: Oxford University Press, 1985), 131-159. See also R. Millward and A. Robinson, 'Stogursey', in *Landscapes of Britain: South-west Peninsula* (Basingstoke: Macmillan, 1971), 179-185.

[10] R. Ballard, *The Priory Church of St Andrew, Stogursey.* 2nd. edn. (Stogursey: Stogursey Parish Council, 1992). Stogursey is one of 34 towns whose plans are analyzed in M. Aston and R. Leech, *Historic Towns in Somerset* (Taunton: Committee for Rescue Archaeology, 1977), 131-135.

[11] Joseph Bettey, 'Somerset parish churches and parishioners during the Middle Ages', in Tom Mayberry and Hilary Binding (eds.), *Somerset: the Millenium Book* (Tiverton: Somerset Books, 1999), 37-50; quotation from p. 37.

[12] The indispensable guide continues to be N. Pevsner, *The Buildings of England: South and West Somerset* (Harmondsworth: Penguin, 1958); a revised edition is in preparation and eagerly awaited. For a selective guide which includes many Somerset churches see R. Dunning, *Fifty Somerset Churches* (Tiverton: Somerset Books, 1996).

[13] J. H. Crothers, *St Mary's Church, Nettlecombe: Guide* (Nettlecombe: Nettlecombe Parish Council, 2003). Fig. 3, p. 5.

[14] R. W. Dunning, *Somerset Monasteries* (Stroud: Tempus, 2001). Classic early accounts are also provided by T. Scott Holmes in his chapters on 'Ecclesiastical history' and 'Religious houses' in Page, 1906 (note 3), 1-67, 68-172.

[15] Adkins & Adkins, 1992 (note 8), 42-43. Detailed plans of the buildings are given in R. Parker *et al*, 'Excavation and building study at Cleeve Abbey, 1995-2003', *Somerset Archaeological and Natural History Society, Proceedings,* **150** (2006), 73-167.

[16] This was the last of Berta Lawrence's eighteen poems published in the *Exmoor Review,* **45** (2004), 23] over a 37-year period from 1967. Over her lifetime, Berta wrote over one hundred poems, many inspired by Somerset (and particularly Exmoor) landscapes, writing her final verses in the week in which she died (at age 97).

[17] Adkins & Adkins, 1992 (note 8), 83; Bush, 1994 (note 2), 124.

[18] Bush, 1994 (note 2), 55.

[19] Bush, 1994 (note 2), 194-6.

[20] In the Middle Ages the word 'hospital' meant a hospice or refuge, often a simple almshouse under a warden.

[21] Among the most useful general sources for this section I have found are the relevant chapters in Michael Aston (ed.), *Aspects of the Medieval Landscape of Somerset* (Taunton: Somerset County Council, 1988); the section of Hazel Riley's monograph on the medieval Quantock Hills landscape, see Riley, 2006 (note 8), 85-114; and the two volumes of the V. C. H. covering much of the Quantocks, viz. R. W. Dunning, (ed.), *Victoria History of the County of Somerset,* Vol. 5. (Oxford: Oxford University Press, 1992) and Dunning, 1985 (note 9).

[22] There are a number of histories of Quantock landowning families. See for example G. O. Stawell, *A Quantock Family. The Stawells of Cothelstone and Their Descendants, the Barons Stawell of Somerton, and the Stawells of Devonshire, and the County Cork* (Taunton: Barnicott and Pearce, 1910) and H. A. Wyndham, *A Family History, 1688-1837: The Wyndhams of Somerset, Sussex and Wiltshire* (Oxford: Oxford University Press, 1950).

[23] Both houses are described in detail in R. Dunning, *Some Somerset Country Houses: A Personal Selection* (Wimborne: Dovecote Press, 1991), 61-66.

[24] P. Haggett, *Agriculture and Land Use in the Quantock Parishes, West Somerset* (Cambridge: B.A. Thesis, 1953), 46-53.

[25] Historical Manuscripts Commission, *Calendar of Manuscripts of the Dean and Chapter of Wells,* see Haggett, 1953 (note 24), 47.

[26] Haggett, 1953 (note 24), 48.

[27] N. F. Hulbert, 'A survey of Somerset fairs', *Somerset Archaeological and Natural History Society, Proceedings,* **82** (1936), 87-117.

[28] E. W. R. Moore, *The Fairs of Medieval England* (Toronto: Pontifical Institute of Medieval Studies, 1985).

[29] Mary Siraut, Robert Dunning and Ken Brown, *The Quantocks: A Past Worth Preserving* (Tiverton: Somerset Books, 1992).

[30] The figures for facilities at Somerset inns in 1686 is taken from Tony Scrase, *Somerset Towns:*

Changing Fortunes, 800-1800 (Strud: Tempus, 2005), 118.

[31] Siraut *et al*, 1992 (note 29), Chapt. 2.

[32] P. Ashford, 'The west Somerset woollen trade, 1500-1714', *Somerset Archaeological and Natural History Society, Proceedings,* **151** (2008), 165-180.

[33] Ashford, 2008 (note 31), pp. 170-171.

[34] Siraut *et al*, 1992 (note 29), 21.

[35] Population estimates for England are taken from tables in D. Cole and J. Salt, *The British Population: Patterns, trends and Processes* (Oxford: Oxford University Press, 1992). The Quantock region has an area 0.0025 that of England and this ratio has been used to estimate, albeit very roughly, the likely Quantock 'share' of totals.

[36] E. H. Bates-Harbin, 'The "black death" in Somerset, 1348-9', *Somerset Archaeological and Natural History Society, Proceeding,* **63** (1917), 89-99. The two classic accounts that refer briefly to the situation in west Somerset are A. E. Levett and A. Ballard, *The Black Death on the Estates of the See of Winchester* (Oxford: Clarendon Press, 1916) and J. F. D. Shrewsbury, *A History of Bubonic Plague in the British Isles* (London: Cambridge University Press, 1970).

[37] Lists of incumbents up to 1730 are given in F. W. Weaver (ed.), *Somerset's Incumbents from the Hugo MSS 30, 279-80 in the British Museum* (Privately printed, 1889).

Five. Early Modern Period

[1] Robin Bush, 'The age of elegance', in Tom Mayberry and Hilary Binding (eds.), *Somerset: The Millennium Book* (Tiverton: Somerset Books, 1999), 79-96; quotation, 79.

[2] T. J. Hunt and R. R. Sellman, *Aspects of Somerset History* (Taunton: Somerset County Council, 1973), 26-27.

[3] Hunt & Sellman, 1973 (note 2), 28-30. Robert Dunning, *A History of Somerset*, 3rd. edn. (Tiverton: Somerset Books, 2003), 75-84.

[4] J. H. Bettey, *Wessex from AD 1000* (London: Longman, 1986), 182-187.

[5] Robert Dunning, *The Monmouth Rebellion: A Complete Guide to the Rebellion and Bloody Assize* (Wimborne: Dovecote Press, 1984). Map of origin of rebels, 62. See also Hunt & Sellman, 1973 (note 2), 31-35

[6] Bettey, 1986 (note 4), 185.

[7] Dunning, 1984 (note 5), 61.

[8] Robert Dunning, *Somerset Families* (Tiverton: Somerset Books, Tiverton, 2002). Seven families with seats in the Quantocks are included amongst the 34 surveyed, viz. the Acland-Hoods (Fairfield), Carews (Crowcombe), Kemeys-Tyntes (Halswell), Luttrells (East Quantoxhead), Stawells (Cothelstone), Trevelyans (Nettlecombe) and Wyndhams (Orchard).

[9] R. Ballard, *The Priory Church of St Andrew, Stogursey.* 2nd. edn. (Stogursey: Stogursey Parish Council, 1992).

[10] D. Ireson, *St Decuman,* Watchet, n.d.

[11] R. W. Dunning, (ed.), *Victoria History of the County of Somerset,* Vol. 5: *Williton and Freemanors Hundred* (Oxford: Oxford University Press, 1992). Nettlecombe Court is described on pp. 114-5 and Orchard Wyndham on pp. 154-155.

[12] Engravings of most of the major Quantock houses by Thomas Bonner were drawn to accompany John Collinson, *History and Antiquities of the County of Somerset*, 3 vols. (Bath, 1791). Standard descriptions of all major country houses in the region are given by N. Pevsner, *The Buildings of England: South and West Somerset* (Harmondsworth: Penguin Books, 1958). Eight Quantock houses are included by Robert Dunning in his *Some Somerset Country Houses: A Personal Selection* (Wimborne: Dovecote Press, 1991), *viz.* Blackmore Farm, the Court House, Enmore Castle, Fairfield, Gothelney, Gurney Street, Halswell House and Orchard Wyndham.

[13] For a definitive account of the great Somerset landscape gardens with accounts of Barford Park, Crowcombe Court, Fairfield, Fyne Court, Halswell, Hestercombe, Nettlecombe Court, Orchard Wyndham, St Audries, Sandhill Park and Terhill, see Tim Mowl and Marion Mako, *Historic Gardens of Somerset* (Bristol: Redcliffe Press, 2010). See also T. Williamson, *Polite*

Landscapes. Gardens and Society in Eighteenth Century England (Stroud: Alan Sutton, 1995). A number of Quantock follies are discussed in J. Holt, *Somerset Follies* (Bath: Akeman Press, 2007).

[14] *Hestercombe Gardens: An Illustrated History and Guide* (Hestercombe: Hestercombe Garden Trust, 2006).

[15] Nat Alcock and Cary Carson, *West Country Farms: House and Estate Surveys, 1598-176.* (Oxford: Oxbow Books, 2007), 146-166 ('Nettlecombe, 1619').

[16] John and Jane Penoyre, *Decorative Plasterwork in the Houses of Somerset, 1500-1700* (Taunton: Somerset County Council, 1994).

[17] Mary Siraut, Robert Dunning and Ken Brown, *The Quantocks: A Past Worth Preserving* (Tiverton: Somerset Books, 1992); E. H. Bates-Harbin, 'Leland in Somersetshire; 1540–1542'. *Somerset Archaeology and Natural History,* **33** (1887), 60-136.

[18] Siraut *et al*, 1992 (note 17), 27.

[19] Siraut *et al*, 1992 (note 17), 32.

[20] Berta Lawrence, *A Somerset Journal* (London: Westaway Books, 1951), 150-151.

[21] D. Warren, *Somerset s Industrial Heritage: A Guide and Gazetteer* (Somerset Industrial Archaeology Society Survey, **8** 1966); M. Palmer and P. Neaverson, *The Textile Industry of South-West England. A Social Archaeology* (Stroud: Tempus, 2005); and P. Ashford, 'The West Somerset woollen trade, 1500-1714', *Somerset Archaeological and Natural History Society, Proceedings,* **151** (2008), 165-180.

[22] Personal communication from Ivor Slocombe (April 2012) who has researched the Bridgwater water bailiff and port book accounts. Brazil wood was recorded there as 'fryan-dobuck', a Somerset corruption of 'Pernambuco', the town in north-east Brazil from which the wood was imported into Portugal and eventually into Bridgwater.

[23] Ashford, 2008 (note 21), 175.

[24] E. T. Jones, 'River navigation in medieval England', *Journal of Historical Geography,* 26 (2000), 60-82.

[25] Appendix B of William Albert, *Turnpike Road System in England, 1663–1840* (Cambridge: Cambridge University Press, 1972) lists all the Acts. For Somerset see J. B. Bentley and B. J. Murless, *Somerset Roads: The Legacy of the Turnpikes, Phase I – Western Somerset* (Somerset Industrial Archaeological Society, 1985).

[26] A useful check list for each county is given in C. R. Humphrey-Smith, *The Phillimore Atlas and Register of Parish Registers* (Chichester: Phillimore, 1984); for Somerset parishes see map and parish index, pp. 216–222.

[27] Both the methods and tables of the results are given in E. A. Wrigley and R. S. Schofield, *The Population History of England 1541-1871: A Reconstruction* (Cambridge: Cambridge University Press, 1989).

[28] J. Oswin, 'The Somerset population prior to the census of 1801', *Somerset Archaeological and Natural History Society, Proceedings,* **145** (2001), 117-125. Tony Scrase, *Somerset Towns: Changing Fortunes 800 -1800* (Stroud: Tempus, 2005), 69-146.

Six. Late Regency and Victorian Landscapes

[1] As displayed on a wall plaque in the railway section of the Tiverton and Mid Devon Museum, Tiverton. Peter Braine tells me that this first railway journey was from Manchester to Liverpool, see L. T. C. Rolt, *Isambard Kingdom Brunel* (London: Longman, 1964), 45.

[2] A full description of stations along the West Somerset Railway is given in M. Oakley, *Somerset Railway Stations* (Wimborne: Dovecote Press, 2002).

[3] This section based on updating of P. Haggett, *Agriculture and Land Use in the Quantock Parishes, West Somerset* (Cambridge: Geographical Tripos, Part I, 1953). The main sources referred to in this section are W. Marshall, *The Rural Economy of the West of England*, reprint of 1787 edition (Newton Abbot: David and Charles, 1970) and John Billingsley, *General View of the Agriculture of the County of Somerset* (Bath: Cruttwell, 1797). A second edition with additional notes was published in 1798. Billingsley's was one of a series of county reports published at this time; see the review by W.G.

East, 'Land utilization in England at the end of the eighteenth century', *Geographical Journal*, **89** (1937), 156-166.

[4] Billingsley, 1797 (note 3), 280.

[5] The definitive work on enclosures is R. J. P. Kain, J. Chapman, and R. R. Oliver, *The Enclosure Maps of England and Wales, 1595-1918* (Cambridge; Cambridge University Press, 2004); see 'Somerset', 182-191.

[6] Map based on two documents in the Somerset Record Office: enclosure award map for 'Crowcombe Heathfield, Heddon, and a Parcel of Quantock Hills', 1780 and tithe apportionment and map for Crowcombe, 1840. See Haggett, 1953 (note 3), 59-63. The definitive reference on tithe maps is R. J. P. Kain and R. R. Oliver, *The Tithe Maps of England and Wales; A Cartographic Analysis and County-by-County Catalogue* (Cambridge: Cambridge University Press, 1995); see 'Somerset', 428-449.

[7] T. D. Acland and W. Sturge, *The Farming of Somersetshire* (London:, 1851).

[8] A review of agricultural sources is given in W. F. Maunder (ed.), *Review of United Kingdom Statistical Sources* (London: Heinemann, 1974).

[9] Map based on comparison of the tithe map and apportionment for Kilve, 1839, compared with the Land Utilization Survey, Sheet 120, surveyed in 1931-32, See Haggett, 1953 (note 3), 73-77.

[10] J. R. Hamilton and J. F. Lawrence, *Men and Mining on the Quantocks*, 2nd. ed. (Exmoor Mines Research Group, 2008).

[11] Berta Lawrence, *Coleridge and Wordsworth in Somerset* (Newton Abbot: David and Charles, 1970).

[12] D. Warren, *Somerset s Industrial Heritage: A Guide and Gazetteer* (Somerset Industrial Archaeology Society Survey, **8**, 1996), 53.

[13] Warren, 1996 (note 12), 24, 59; Hazel Riley, *The Historic Landscape of the Quantock Hills* (Swindon: English Heritage, 2006), 145-147.

[14] Robin Bush, *Somerset: The Complete Guide* (Wimborne: Dovecote Press, 1994), 77-78

[15] Riley, 2006 (note 13), 138-145.

[16] There is a rich array of books on railway history in the area, viz.. P. Stanier, *Somerset* in *the Age of Steam* (Tiverton: Somerset Books, 2003); Oakley, 2001 (note 2); E. T. Macdermot, rev. by C. R. Clinker, *History of the Great Western Railway*, Vol. 2 (Cheltenham: Allen, 1964), 68-102; and D. St. J. Thomas, *Regional History of the Railways of Great Britain: Volume 1 West Country* (Newton Abbot: David and Charles, 1981). Specific books on the West Somerset line include Richard Jones, *West Somerset Railway: A View from the Past* (Cheltenham: Ian Allan, 1998) and Ian Coleby, *Minehead Branch 1848-1971* (Sittingbourne: Lightmoor Press, 2011).

[17] A useful summary of the Brendon Hills iron working is given in Warren, 1996 (note 12), 53-56. See also R. J. Sellick, *The Old Mineral Line* (Dulverton: Exmoor Press, 1981) and R. Madge, *Railways around Exmoor* (Dulverton: Exmoor Press, 1971). A definitive new history is the splendid *Brendon Hills and West Somerset Mineral Railway*, by M. H. Jones (Sittingbourne: Lightmoor Press, 2011).

[18] Warren, 1996 (note 12); I. Coleby, 'The development of Watchet harbour in the 1850s', in A. J. Webb (ed.) *A Maritime History of Somerset. Vol. 1:, Trade and Commerce* (Taunton: Somerset Archaeological and Natural History Society, 2010), 117-134; Bush, 1994 (note 12), 213-214; and G. Farr, *Somerset Harbours* (London: Christopher Johnson, 1954), 119-137. For a highly readable account of Watchet, see W. H. Norman, *Tales of Watchet Harbour* (Watchet, 1988).

[19] R. W. Dunning, (ed.), *Victoria History of the County of Somerset*, Vol. 5: *Williton and Freemanors Hundred* (Oxford: Oxford University Press, 1992), 103-104.

[20] Plans for the canal were lodged by 'Mr Telford and Capt. Nicholls', *Ship Canal for the Junction of the English and Bristol Channels* (London: Brooke, 1824) and the case against by 'Several Gentlemen Opposed to the Measure', *Observations on the Projected Ship Canal from Stolford in the County of Somerset to Beer in the County of Devon* (Sherborne: Harker & Penny, 1824). General reviews are given in T. J. Hunt and R. R. Sellman, *Aspects of Somerset History* (Taunton: Somerset

County Council, 1973), 43-46; Charles Hadfield, *The Canals of South West England* (Newton Abbott: David and Charles, 1967); and Tony Haskell, *By Waterways to Taunton* (Wellington: Somerset Books, 1994)..

[21] A cameo of Lord Taunton's Quantock Estate is given in Mary Siraut, Robert Dunning and Ken Brown, *The Quantocks: A Past Worth Preserving* (Tiverton: Somerset Books, 1992), 34-35.

[22] N. Pevsner, *The Buildings of England: South and West Somerset* (Harmondsworth: Penguin, 1958); Bush, 1994 (note 12), 114.

[23] An account of the mental hospital in Bishops Lydeard is given in D. Hinton and F. Clarke, *The Tone Vale Story* (Taunton: Somerset County Council, 1997).

[24] G. S. Michin, 'Table of Somerset population, 1801-1901', in W. Page (ed.), *Victoria History of the County of Somerset, Vol. 2.* (London: University of London, 1906), 338-353.

Seven. The Twentieth Century

[1] The rectangular plaque in Cannington church also contains the regimental shield. The role of American forces in the county in World War II is described in M. Hawkins, *Somerset at War, 1939-1945* (Wimborne: Dovecote Press, 1996), 115-121.

[2] Tom Mayberry, 'Modern times', in Tom Mayberry and Hilary Binding (eds), *Somerset: The Millennium Book* (Tiverton: Somerset Books, 1999), 127-139; see, 127.

[3] Robin Bush, *Somerset: The Complete Guide* (Wimborne: Dovecote Press, 1994), 114.

[4] *Hestercombe Gardens: An Illustrated History and Guide* (Hestercombe: Hestercombe Gardens Trust, 2006), 2; T. Mowl and M. Mako, *Historic Gardens of Somerset* (Bristol: Redcliffe Press, 2010), 213-216.

[5] Mayberry 1999 (note 2), 131. For a general review which sets the period in context see J. H. Bettey, *Wessex from AD 1000* (London: Longman, 1986), 284-291 ('The Great War and its aftermath').

[6] A copy of the Wells document was published as *Somerset County War Memorial* (Taunton: Goodman and Sons, 1923). These losses are likely to be underestimates as the official War Office total for Somerset-born deaths are 11,300, higher than the Wells total. Battle losses by the county regiment are given in Liz Grant, *The Somerset Light Infantry (Prince Albert's) 1685-1959* (Tiverton: Somerset Books, 2004), 73-106 ('The Great War, 1914-18').

[7] Descriptions of the Quantock forest are given in N. Bannister, 'Quantock forest: an example of multiple land use', *Forestry* **41** (1968), 15-26 and *Quantock Forest Trail* (Over Stowey: Forestry Commission, 1960). See also P. Wolseley and E. Neal, *Quantock Wildlife: Its Ecology and Conservation* (Broomfield: Somerset Trust for Nature Conservation, 1980), 12-15.

[8] J. Skudder, 'Kilve and the West Somerset oilfield'. *Journal of the West Somerset Village History Society* **31** (2006), 7-23.

[9] For a summary of the Somerset findings see T. Stuart-Menteath, *Somerset: Land Utilization Survey Report,* **86.** (London: Land Utilization Survey, 1938). Results for the whole country are summarized in L. Dudley Stamp, *The Land of Britain: Its Use and Misuse* (London: Longmans Green, 1948). My own copy of Sheet 120 ('Bridgwater and the Quantock Hills') was given to me by my old primary-school teacher, Miss Helen Carter, who organized the field survey for her own parish.

[10] Others built since World War II include the small Hawkridge Reservoir (32 acres) in Spaxton Parish from east-flowing Quantock streams and the very large Clatworthy Reservoir (130 acres) on the western edge of our area from south-flowing tributaries of the Tone.

[11] The definitive account with many useful appendices is given in Mac Hawkins fine survey *Somerset at War* (note 1). This is supplemented by J. Hurley, *Exmoor in Wartime, 1939-45* (Dulverton: Exmoor Press, 1978) and Hazel Riley, *The Historic Landscape of the Quantock Hills* (Swindon: English Heritage, 2006), 153-159.

[12] *Hestercombe at War: An Illustrated History and Guide* (Hestercombe: Hestercombe Gardens Trust, 2007).

[13] Hawkins 1996 (note 1), 209-210.

[14] The earliest Somerset planning report was by W. Harding Thompson in 1934. That the Scott Report should have been written at the height of the Blitz says something of the concern for the future of rural England; see the comments of one of its influential members, L. Dudley Stamp, 'The Scott report', *Geographical Journal*, 101 (1943), 16-20. Since the 1947 Act, planning reports have poured out at county, district and regional levels of administration. One of the earliest was County Planning Department, *Somerset: County Development Plan* (Taunton: Somerset County Council, 1953).

[15] Background material on the nuclear question is given in M. Barnes, *The Hinkley Point Public Inquiries: A Report* (London: HMSO, 1990). See also J. Glasson, *et al*, 'A local income and employment multiplier analysis of a proposed nuclear power station development at Hinkley Point in Somerset', *Urban Studies*, **25** (1988), 248-261.

[16] Bracey's pioneering work on Somerset was summarized in H. E. Bracey, 'Towns as rural service centres: an index of centrality with special reference to Somerset', *Institute of British Geographers, Transactions and Papers*, **19** (1953), 95-105; and H. E. Bracey, 'English central villages: identification, distribution, and functions', in K. Norborg (ed.) *Proceedings of the IGU Symposium in Urban Geography, Lund 1960* (Lund: Studies in Geography, **B24**, 1962), 169-190. The follow-up work by Liz Mills was summarized in P. Haggett, E. A. Mills, and M. A. Morgan, *An Atlas of Rural Services in Somerset and South Avon, 1950-1980: A Preliminary Analysis* (Bristol: Report to Social Science Research Council, 1983), 1-44 and given in full in E. A. Mills, *Changes in the Spatial Economy of an English County: Somerset, 1950-1980* (Doctoral dissertation, University of Bristol, 1989).

[17] Bracey, 1962 (note 16), 178.

[18] As a Methodist, I recall attending circuit rallies at King Street Methodist Church in Bridgwater whose territory included the eastern chapels in the Quantocks. Sadly, King Street is now a storehouse and many of the small chapels have gone.

[19] Sedgemoor District Council, *Sedgemoor Landscape Assessment and Countryside Design Summary* (Bridgwater, 2003).

[20] Good accounts of the branch line, its closure, and its restoration are given in C. G. Maggs, *The Minehead Branch and the West Somerset Railway* (Usk: Oakwood Press, 1998); Richard Jones, *West Somerset Railway: A View from the Past* (Shepperton: Ian Allan, 1998); and I. Coleby, *The Minehead Branch 1848-1971* (Witney: Lightmoor Press, 2006).

[21] Somerset County Council, Environment Department, 1991 *Census District Ward Profiles for Sedgemoor, Taunton Deane and West Somerset Districts* (Taunton: Somerset County Council, 1993).

Eight. *Epilogue*: Quantock Futures

[1] William Wordsworth, 'Lines composed a few miles above Tintern Abbey on revisiting the banks of the Wye during a tour, 13 July 1798'. It first appeared as the last poem in the 1798 edition of the *Lyrical Ballads*.

[2] For a general view of rapid shift of climates see S. Barker, *et al*, '800,000 years of abrupt climate variability', *Science*, **334** (2011), 347-351.

[3] At the start of the new millennium many Quantock parishes issued documents to celebrate the event. Some like *Cannington Reflection* were locally produced. Others were published by commercial houses such as Halsgrove and include volumes on Blue Anchor, Bicknoller, Crowcombe, Elworthy, Monksilver, Nettlecombe, St Audries, Sampford Brett, Stogumber, Watchet and Williton. Together they represent a formidable addition to the Quantock literature; see M. McDermott, 'Somerset millennium books', *Somerset Archaeological and Natural History Society, Proceedings,* **144** (2000), 197-206.

[4] P. F. Ulf-Hansen and D. C. Boyce, *Exmoor and the Quantock Hills: Natural Area Profile.* (English Nature, 1997); P. Wolseley and E. Neal, *Quantock Wildlife: Its Ecology and Conservation* (Broomfield: Somerset Trust for Nature Conservation, 1980), 4-7.

[5] Wolseley & Neal, 1980 (note 5), 8-11. Quantock Hills AONB Joint Advisory Committee, 'Forestry and woodlands', *Management Plan, 2009-2014* (Broomfield: AONB, 2009), 31-40.

[6] See section on 'hunting' in W. Page (ed.), *Victoria History of the County of Somerset, Vol. 1*. (London: University of London, 1906), 383-433 and Quantock Deer Management and Conservation Group, *Sustainable Management and Conservation of Deer on the Quantock* (Nether Stowey: AONB, 2006). A broad review is given in J. Langbein and R. Putnam, *Conservation and Management of Deer on Exmoor and the Quantocks* (Southampton: Southampton University, 1992).

[7] Quantock Hills AONB Joint Advisory Committee, 'Visitors and recreation', *Management Plan, 2009-2014* (Broomfield: AONB, 2009), 57-64. The AONB service publish small pamphlets (with maps) on circular walks that can be followed from the four 'high' car parks at Staple Plain, Dead Woman's Ditch, Lydeard Hill and Cothelstone.

[8] I. Bright and R. Filler, *Quantock Cycle Rides* (Bridgwater: Sedgmoor District Council, 2000).

[9] G. Davey (ed.), *Diocesan Directory: Bath and Wells, 2008* (Wells: Diocesan Board of Finance, 2007).

[10] Jack Ayres (ed.), *Paupers and Pig Killers: The Diary of William Holland, A Somerset Parson, 1799–1818* (Stroud: Sutton, 1984).

[11] Rankings of church architecture is contentious. The three sources I've used here are Simon Jenkins, *England's Thousand Best Churches* (London: Penguin, 1999); R. Dunning, *Fifty Somerset Churches* (Tiverton: Somerset Books, 1996); and the stars given to parish churches in R. Bush, *Somerset: The Complete Guide* (Wimborne: The Dovecote Press, 1994).

[12] EDF Energy, *Hinkley Point C: Proposed Nuclear Development (Preferred Proposals)* (London: EDF Energy, 2010).

[13] Details of the Bridgwater Bay scheme are given in *Severn Tidal Power Feasibility Study: Conclusions and Summary Report* (London: HMSO, 2010). For a general review of potentials and problems see P. Haggett and A. G. Hoare, 'Tidal power and estuary management: a geographical perspective', in R.T. Severn, *et al*, (eds.) *Tidal Power and Estuary Management* (Bristol: Scientechnica, 1979), 14-25.

[14] Dorothy Wordsworth records many parts of this walk with her brother and Coleridge in a score of entries in her *Alfoxden Journal*. The entry for February 3rd 1798 recalls the dramatic view from Dowsborough: 'I never saw such a vision of earth, sky and sea'. Poems on the walk were later written by Thomas Folliott, *The Quantock Hils: Stanzas Written in the Neighbourhood of Holford* (London: Fifield, 1906). Hazlitt recalls from a visit in 1798 that Coleridge 'seemed unable to keep on a strait line', dodging from one side of the hill path to the other while Wordsworth preferred to compose while walking up and down a level gravel-walk as at Alfoxton; see Lucy Newlyn, 'Hazlitt and Edward Thomas on walking', *Essays in Criticism*, **56** (2006), 163-187.

[15] Jenny Graham is one of a group of contemporary Somerset artists who draw inspiration from the Quantock landscape and regularly exhibit in that area, notably in the regular September 'Somerset Artists' fortnight. They include Annabel Gaitskell Anderson, Leo Davey, Clare DuVergier, Marilyn Ewens, Juliet Harkness, Alison Jacob, Tom Jacob, Rosie Smith and Barry Watkin. The copy of Jenny Graham's 'Towards Wales', on our hall landing is not the original canvas but Number 1/1 of the print.

[16] Sadly, Arthur Ransome confined his children's adventures set in England to the Lake District (e.g. *Pigeon Post*) and East Anglia (e.g. *Coot Club*). But he apologized for 'not blundering onto the West Country moors' in a long and generous preface to a remarkable adventure book (*The Far Distant Oxus*, London: Jonathan Cape, 1937) set on Exmoor. It was written by two schoolgirls, Katharine Hull (aged 15) and Pamela Whitlock (16), and remains a nostalgic 1930s period-piece written in the Ransome style.

Place Index

This index emphasizes Quantock places and aims to serve as a gazetteer for visitors to the area. The 35 parishes which make up the region (see Fig. 1.15) are given in CAPITALS with cross references to important locations set within them. 'Church' refers to parish church unless otherwise stated. 'Families' refer to long-term landowning families with special links to Quantock places. Numbers in **bold** font at the end of page references refer to plates in the separate colour-photograph section.